SERVOMECHANISMS

SERVOMECHANISMS
Devices and Fundamentals

RICHARD W. MILLER
State University of New York
Canton Agricultural and Technical College

RESTON PUBLISHING COMPANY, Inc., Reston, Virginia
A Prentice-Hall Company

Library of Congress Cataloging in Publication Data

Miller, Richard W
   Servomechanisms : devices & fundamentals.

   Bibliography: p.
   1. Servomechanisms.
TJ214.M48   629.8'32   76-58013
ISBN 0-87909-760-4

© 1977 by Richard W. Miller

10 9 8 7 6 5 4 3 2 1

Printed in the United States of America

This book is dedicated to my wife, Irene, for her patience and understanding and to all those students who participated and contributed in one way or another to the development of this text and laboratory experiments over the past few years.

Contents

Preface

The purpose of this textbook is to provide material for a course in servomechanisms given to electrical or mechanical technology students at the two-year college level. It is more hardware oriented than mathematically oriented so that it might be used in some engineering schools. It will also give a technician or a practicing engineer in industry an up-to-date refresher course. Approximately 60 percent of the material concentrates on the different devices that are used to make up a complete servo system, especially those devices that are used as transducers and/or error detectors and correctors.

Basic theory in electricity/electronics, machines, amplifiers, power supplies, and the like has not been covered because most curricula in electrical or mechanical technology have done this adequately in other courses. For the same reasons, only enough physics has been presented to make the reader aware of the effects of velocity, acceleration, torque, inertia, and friction in a servo system. Analysis of simple linear servo systems is done without a rigorous mathematical approach. The differential equation for such systems is derived only to emphasize the effects of inertia and friction on system performance under change of input signal or when an external disturbance occurs. The conversion from the time domain to frequency domain is done algebraically by using the "s" operator as a tool only, and then by converting to the "jW" operation. Finally, the Bode plot is used to analyze and to predict system performance of such systems.

One chapter deals with some of the different servo trainers now on the market for laboratory use. These trainers are basically of a modular type with greater emphasis on devices and hardware than on the mathematical equivalent. Their adaptability to a laboratory is only limited by the imagination of the user. Several representative experiments follow at the end of the text to illustrate what can be done with a trainer. The author has available for perusal a complete, separate laboratory manual for this textbook in which experimental procedures, recommended apparatus and equipment, and analysis of results are presented. The combination of this textbook and the laboratory manual comprise a four-credit-hour one-semester course in basic servomechanism theory.

The author wishes to thank all the companies who sent him technical information with permission to use what he could. The companies are: Schaevitz Engineering; Bourns, Inc.; New England Instrument Co.; Control Data Corporation; Feedback, Inc.; Reeves Instrument Corp.; American Electronics Inc.; Helipot of Beckman Instruments, Inc.; Automatic Timing and Controls Co.; Muirhead Instruments Ltd.; Astrosystems, Inc.; Pro-Log Corp.; Chilton Technological Services, Digiac Corp. In addition, publications from the United States Navy were also used. The electrical specifications for the potentiometer section were taken from the Variable Resistive Components Institute, Revision A 1974 Industry Standard.

RICHARD W. MILLER

ONE

Introduction to systems

1.1. GENERAL

Automatic control is used in many processes and applications, for example, to control the temperature of a furnace, the rolling of a sheet of steel, the machine tool in a milling process, the launching and maneuvering of a space vehicle, as well as in a myriad of other industrial, commercial and military applications. In many of these applications, the term "servomechanism" is becoming more and more a part of the total control package, whether it is an instrument servo, a control servo, or a power servo. The term *servomechanism* is a combination of two words: one from the Latin, *servus*, meaning a slave or servant, and the other word being "mechanism." Thus it is a mechanism that slaves or serves to carry out the commands that it is given. Specifically, the term servomechanism means a control system in which the controlled quantity is "mechanical position."

One of the earliest applications of automatic control, and to a certain extent a servomechanism, was the flyball governor invented by James Watt in 1788 to control the speed of a steam engine. Although this governor was not very accurate due to oscillations and instability, it still did work, and it was gradually improved. As time passed, more and more advances were made by many different people, though somewhat slowly. The advent of World War II was really the turning point in the automatic control field. This was especially true in the military field where the control of ships, submarines, aircraft, radar systems, etc., greatly accelerated the study, advancement, and practice of the servomechanism.

Automatic control systems may be open-loop or open-cycle in nature, or they may be closed-loop or closed-cycle. The general term *feedback control system* encompasses the latter; in such a system, feedback is used to compare the controlled quantity against a reference quantity. The comparison between these two determines whether or not the controlled variable (which might be, for example, temperature, pressure, fluid flow, speed, torque, or mechanical position) is at the desired value. This comparison is performed by a transducer, which is simply a device that converts energy from one form to another; that is, mechanical position is converted to electrical voltage via a potentiometer or motor speed is converted to electrical voltage via a tachometer-generator. Regardless of the type of variable, if the controlled output is not at its desired value, then the device(s) used for comparison create(s) an error signal which is fed to an amplifier, which in turn feeds an error-correcting device of some nature, which then drives the system to restore the variable to the desired value. In a servomechanism a motor would be used as the error-correcting device. Once the system has been brought within its tolerance band or accuracy limits, it will stay that way until some outside disturbance again causes an error signal to be created telling the system to correct itself once more.

1.2.   CONTROL

In general, three types of control can be performed to position a load or to control the rate at which a load is moved from one speed level to another. These three types are (1) ON-OFF control, (2) stepwise control, and (3) continuous control.

Figure 1-1 shows a switch controlling a motor. When the switch is closed, "ON" control results. When the switch is open, "OFF" control results.

Figure 1-2 shows a rheostat with definite taps controlling power to a load. Each individual tap provides an increase of load voltage in a definite step, fashion, hence the name *stepwise* control.

Figure 1-3 shows a precision potentiometer controlling a motor. The wiper makes contact at practically every turn resulting in a continuous flow of power; hence the name *continuous* control.

In any of these systems, if the output has no effect on the input, then it is known as an open-loop or open-cycle system. When the output can be fed back into the system so that it affects the input, it is known as a closed-loop or closed-cycle system. Regardless of the system, whether it be open-loop or closed-loop, a block diagram will simplify the understanding and analysis of it, no matter how complex it is.

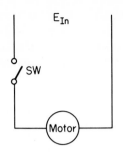

On—Off

FIG 1-1.

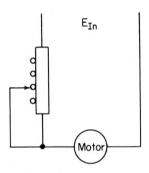

Stepwise

FIG. 1-2.

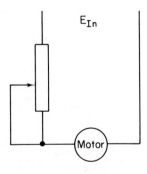

Continuous

FIG. 1-3.

1.3. BLOCK DIAGRAMS

A block diagram is a shorthand method of showing how one quantity depends on another. A generalized block diagram is shown in figure 1-4.

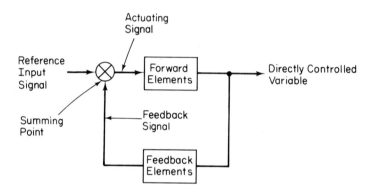

FIG. 1-4. Generalized Block Diagram of a Closed Loop System

A simple proportional servo, however, may be better represented by the block diagram of figure 1-5. Using as an example a mechanical positioning system, the blocks shown represent the following elements:

1. The *input element* provides the reference input signal which initiates and governs the response of the system. This is the reference against

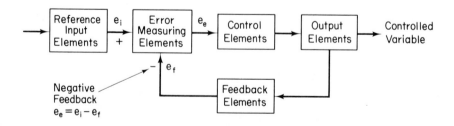

FIG. 1-5. Expanded Block Diagram of a Closed Loop System

which the actual performance of the system is compared. It is some-times called the *command,* and it may be a reference voltage from a potentiometer, a linear transducer, a synchro transmitter, or a tachometer.

2. The *output element* is that part of the system which actually produces the output being controlled, and it is acted on by the other com-ponents. It is also referred to as *directly controlled variable* or *controlled system.* In a servomechanism this would be a function of mechanical position or rate.

3. The *error-measuring element* is a comparator, an error detector or a summation junction which compares the instantaneous values of the reference input and the controlled output. This junction can be a resistance network, an impedance network, etc., and may even be contained within an amplifier.

4. The *control element* consists of all the parts of the system which have any effect on the controlled output. This element contains the power amplifiers needed in the system, the power inputs, all the control elements which have an effect on control windings of devices, grid control of a tube, base control of a transistor, etc.

5. The *feedback element* is the device that converts the controlled output into a feedback signal which is an analog of the output. This signal must be of the same form and scale as the signal from the reference. The difference between the two signals is the error.

A truer picture of a servomechanism using an electric motor as the actuator is that represented in figure 1-6. Most of the functional blocks

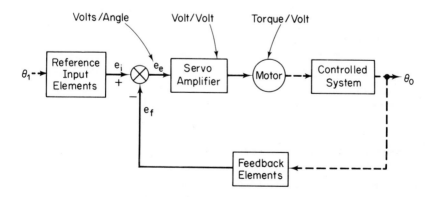

FIG. 1-6. Electrical Summing Junction Block Diagram

have been kept, but the error measuring elements block and control elements block have been replaced with the summation junction symbol, an amplifier and a motor. The true variable of a servomechanism is a mechanical shaft angle; thus a dotted line is used with the output designated as θ_0. A mechanical shaft angle must then be the reference input or command, θ_1. The reference input and feedback elements convert these mechanical signals into electrical signals. Electromechanical transducers such as precision potentiometers, variable reluctance transducers, resolvers and synchros perform these conversions.

In order to convert the block diagram of figure 1-6 into a representation of a rate servo, all that is needed is to change the input and the output to the first derivative of position, *i.e.*, speed.

1.4. CLOSED-LOOP APPLICATIONS

The following figures, figures 1-7, 1-8 and 1-9, show three different closed-loop systems featuring feedback from output to input. The characteristics of all these systems are (1) fast response, (2) high accuracy—lack of error or deviation, and (3) stability under dynamic responses.

Figure 1-7(a) shows the schematic wiring for a dc generator with an exciter. The voltage across the field of the exciter is the difference between the reference voltage and the feedback voltage from the generator armature. If load is suddenly increased on the generator, the generator voltage will tend to decrease, thereby increasing the differential between the reference and the load voltage. This means that there is a larger voltage across the field of the exciter, and that the voltage output of the exciter is increased. This increased exciter voltage increases the generator field current, which in turn raises the generator output voltage back to its present value. Figure 1-7(b) shows the block diagram; separate blocks represent different parts of the circuit.

Figure 1-8(a) shows the schematic diagram for a dc motor that controls the tension of roofing material on a reel drive. In this system, the roofing paper is a continuous strip and must be rolled on a reel at a constant tension. If the tension increases, the paper may tear; if the tension decreases, the layers of paper on the roll become very loose.

As the reel builds up with paper, the tension on the paper would increase if the speed were kept constant; thus the reel speed must be controlled to maintain a constant tension. The desired tension is set by the weight of the rider under which the paper runs. The rider can move only vertically. The roofing paper supports the rider; therefore, any change in tension moves the rider either up or down. It moves up for

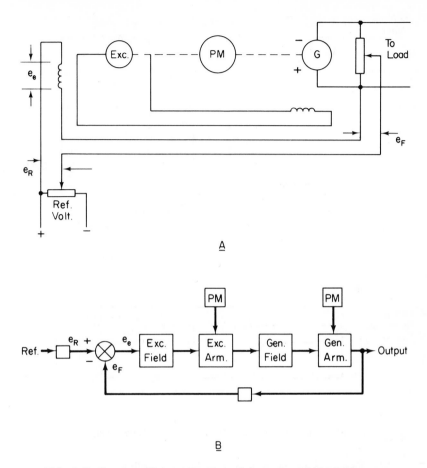

FIG. 1-7. Generator Voltage Regulator Schematic and Block Diagram

increased tension and down for decreased tension. Figure 1-8(b) presents the block diagram.

Figure 1-9(a) shows the schematic diagram of a gun control servomechanism where range direction is the controlled parameter. A synchro pair—a transmitter CX and a control transformer CT—is used to detect and provide the error signal. An amplidyne is used to provide the excitation to the armature of the dc driving motor because of its very fast response and high amplification. This amplification means that the fields of the amplidyne can be supplied from an electronic amplifier, either tube or solid state, because the fields do not require very much power. The input to the amplifier is the "error" signal which indicates how far out of line the actual gun position is in respect to the desired position.

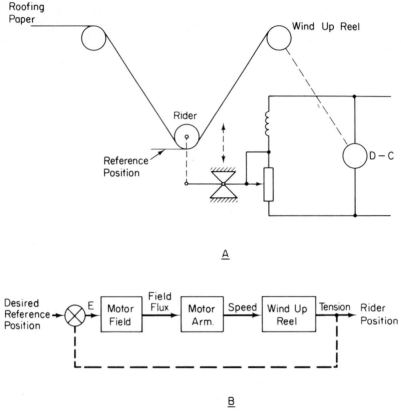

A

B

FIG. 1-8. Tension Control Schematic and Block Diagram

The operation of the system is basically as follows:

1. Everything is at rest; the gun is pointing at an angle of 0°; and the synchros are at null with zero error voltage.
2. Suddenly an airplane appears at 30° from the null.
3. The synchro transmitter is turned 30°; there is now a difference between the CX and CT stator voltages; thus, an output voltage from the CT results. This error voltage is amplified and fed to the proper amplidyne field which generates a different voltage in the amplidyne.
4. The generated voltage in the amplidyne has such a polarity that it drives the motor in the proper direction and reduces the error voltage to zero.

Figure 1-9(b) is the block diagram.

In all of these systems, the return of the output to the desired point will probably result in overshooting or hunting. Stabilizing a servo system

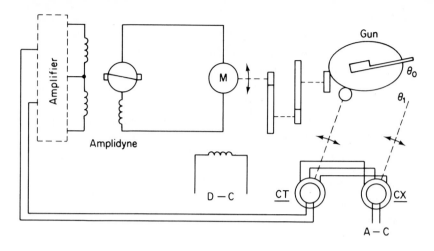

A

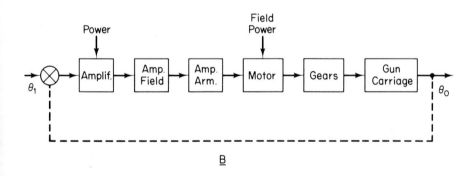

B

FIG. 1-9. Gun Control Schematic and Block Diagram

to prevent or control this overshooting is one of the hardest things to design into a servomechanism.

QUESTIONS AND PROBLEMS

1. Identify the input and output of the following devices or systems and draw a block diagram for each:
   (a) an automatic refrigerator
   (b) Sunbeam "Radiant Toast" toaster

(c) a man shooting a deer
(d) a man driving an automobile
(e) an automatic washing machine
(f) a gas furnace controlled by a thermostat
(g) the perspiration system of a human being
(h) an automobile power-steering apparatus

2. A subtractive summing point in a feedback-control loop means that negative feedback is being employed. Why is this true?

3. Define the following terms:
(a) actuating signal
(b) feedback signal
(c) forward loop
(d) reference input
(e) servomechanism
(f) transducer
(g) summing junction

4. What device must be used between the controlled variable and the reference if their forms of energy are not the same?

5. Which of the following devices are transducers? Identify the input and output of each.
(a) a hydraulic jack
(b) a thermocouple
(c) a common distribution transformer
(d) a rack and pinion device
(e) a voltmeter
(f) a vee-belt over a pair of pulleys
(g) a PNP transistor

TWO

Precision potentiometers

2.1. INTRODUCTION

The wire-wound potentiometer has been utilized as an electro-mechanical shaft transducer in electrical systems and instruments for well over 50 years. With the advancement of servomechanism theory and the demand by the military for precise electromechanical shaft transducers, the wire-wound potentiometer has become a very sophisticated device.

2.2. DEFINITION AND SCHEMATIC

What is a precision potentiometer? The Variable Resistive Components Institute defines it as a mechanical-electrical transducer the operation of which depends on the position of a moving contact (wiper) relative to a resistance element. It delivers, to a high degree of accuracy, a voltage output that is some specified function of the applied voltage and shaft position.

A wire-wound precision potentiometer is characterized by a resistance element which is made up of turns of wire on which the wiper makes contact on only a small portion of each turn.

The schematic for a simple wire-wound potentiometer is shown in figures 2-1(a) and 2-1(b). However, for the sake of simplicity, we will use the schematic in figure 2-1(a) throughout this discussion.

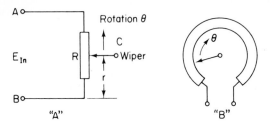

FIG. 2-1. Potentiometer Schematic Diagrams

2.3. MECHANICAL CONSTRUCTION

The essential details of one company's design of a wire-wound potentiometer are shown in figures 2-2(a) and 2-2(b). The mounting plate is made of aluminum; the shaft is of nonmagnetic stainless steel; the bearings of stainless steel and are precision made; the housing of brass, aluminum, or plastic; and the terminals of brass with a gold finish. The brush arm assembly has contacts of precious metal. The resistance element consists of a precious-metal alloy or a nickel-chrome alloy wound on a

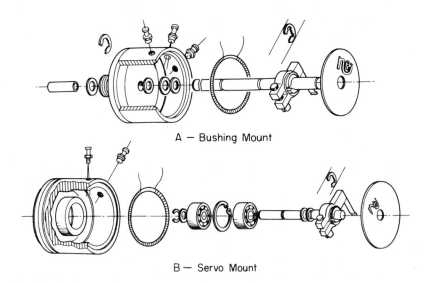

A — Bushing Mount

B — Servo Mount

FIG. 2-2. Exploded Views of Wire-wound Potentiometer Construction (*Courtesy of New England Instrument Co., Natick, Mass.*)

copper mandrel to provide for a uniform winding of precisely spaced turns.

The servo mount shown in figure 2-2(b) is characterized by accuracy, long life, low torque and high reliability, and it is usually motor driven. The type of bushing mount shown in figure 2-2(a) is usually operated manually and is used where preciseness is not too important. Thus precision sleeve bearings may be used in place of ball bearings.

The overall size of a potentiometer is determined by a number of factors. Table 2-1 shows how these factors change as the diameter increases:

TABLE 2-1

ACCURACY	improves
RESOLUTION	improves
POWER RATING	improves
RESISTANCE RANGE	improves
TORQUE	increases
SIZE-WEIGHT	increases
NONLINEAR CAPABILITY	improves

2.4. ROTATION

When the mandrel of a potentiometer is made as shown in figure 2-3, it is known as a *single-turn potentiometer*. When a stop mechanism is built into the potentiometer construction, the rotation of the shaft will be limited to an angle less than 360°. The mechanical angle with stops can be any angle desired, *e.g.*, 270°, 300°, 320°, 330°, 335°, 345°.

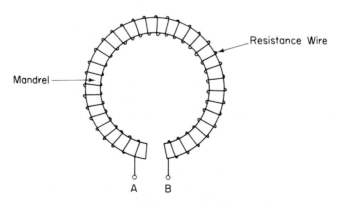

FIG. 2-3. Single-turn Potentiometer Mandrel

When an angle of 360° or more is required, the mandrel can be bent downward at the end, and it can even be continued in the form of a helix. A winding of three turns, five turns, ten turns or even more can thus be obtained. A unit built in such a manner is called a *multiturn potentiometer*. When only a single turn is used, the unit is called a *single-turn continuous-rotation potentiometer*. There is quite a difference between how the brush arm assembly is built in the single-turn and multiturn units. In a single-turn potentiometer, the wiper can be pinned or clamped to the input shaft so that it turns only with the shaft. However in a multiturn potentiometer, the slider must move along the axis of the shaft as well as turn on the shaft so that it will continue to contact the helical winding as the shaft moves. The design of multiturn potentiometers varies, but there must be translatory motion as well as rotary motion of the slider.

2.5. MATHEMATICAL RELATIONS

Let us look at figure 2-1(a) for the following analysis. A potentiometer can be considered "linear" if the resistance per unit length of turn is constant. Thus:

$$a = \frac{r}{R} = \frac{\theta}{\theta_T}, \quad \text{or } r = aR \quad \text{and} \quad r = \frac{\theta}{\theta_T} R \qquad (2\text{-}1)$$

where *a* can only equal or be less than one. If R is assumed to have a value of one, then r equals a in per unit.

When viewed from the voltage point of view, the potentiometer is a simple divider with an output voltage measured between the slider or wiper to one end. Thus:

$$e_0 = \frac{r}{R} E_{IN} = \frac{\theta}{\theta_T} E_{IN} = aE_{IN} \qquad (2\text{-}2)$$

When viewed as a black box, a potentiometer may be represented as in figure 2-4. The transfer function relating these is $E_0/E_{IN} = \theta/\theta_T$ and should be clearly given for all areas of interest. A few examples are

$$\frac{E_0}{E_{IN}} = \frac{\theta}{\theta_T} \text{ Linear } 0 \leq \theta \leq \theta_T \qquad (2\text{-}3)$$

$$\frac{E_0}{E_{IN}} = \text{SINE } \theta \text{ Sine Function } 0 \leq \theta \leq 360° \qquad (2\text{-}4)$$

$$\frac{E_0}{E_{IN}} = \left(\frac{\theta}{\theta_T}\right)^2 \quad \text{Square Function } 0 \le \theta \le \theta_T \qquad (2\text{-}5)$$

$$\frac{E_0}{E_{IN}} = 10^2 \left(\frac{\theta^{-1}}{\theta_T}\right) \quad \text{20dB Log Function } 0 \le \theta \le \theta_T \qquad (2\text{-}6)$$

The potentiometer, then, is used to convert a mechanical change in shaft position to a corresponding electrical signal or vice versa. Because of its ability to convert one form of energy to another, the potentiometer is considered a transducer.

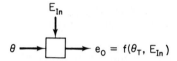

FIG. 2-4. Potentiometer Block Diagram

2.6. LOAD RESISTANCE

A precision potentiometer with the load it is driving is depicted in figure 2-5. This load resistance will introduce an error in the output voltage e_0 which depends on the relative sizes of the load resistance and the potentiometer resistance. A change in output voltage results when the current drawn by the load resistance flows through the series portion of the potentiometer; thus, the voltage drop across this portion changes, with a resultant change in load voltage e_0.

Loading errors for different values of R_L are shown in table 2-2 and can be proven by using calculus. The error difference also depends on

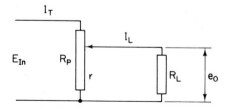

FIG. 2-5. Potentiometer Driving a Load

whether the potentiometer is connected in a single-ended or double-ended circuit.

TABLE 2-2

	Percent Error	
R_L to R_P Proportion	Single-Ended	Double-Ended
$R_L = R_P$	14.8	19.2
$R_L = 10R_P$	1.48	1.92
$R_L = 100R_P$	0.148	0.192

2.7. ELECTRICAL SPECIFICATIONS— WIRE-WOUND POTENTIOMETERS

It is essential to know a number of different electrical characteristics in order to understand and specify potentiometers. These include: resolution (travel, voltage, theoretical), linearity/conformity (terminal-based, zero-based, independent), resistance tolerance, tap location, power rating, noise, starting and running torque, moment of inertia, ac characteristics, and electrical overtravel.

RESOLUTION—This parameter is a measure of the sensitivity to which the output ratio may be set. Figure 2-6 shows the resolution for a wire-wound potentiometer.

In a wire-wound potentiometer, as the slider moves along the winding, it may touch each turn of wire at only one point. As this happens, the slider bounces off the winding so that the voltage varies in steps, rather than in a smooth linear fashion. The plot for this is shown in figure 2-7; from this plot, the various definitions of resolution are obtained.

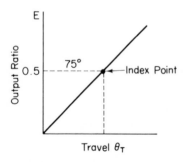

FIG. 2-6. Ideal Resolution

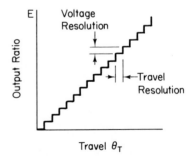

FIG. 2-7. Actual Resolution

1. *Travel resolution* is the maximum value of shaft travel in one direction per incremental voltage step in any specified portion of the winding;
2. *Voltage resolution* is the maximum incremental change in output ratio with shaft travel in one direction in any specified portion of the winding;
3. *Theoretical resolution* is the reciprocal of the number of turns in the actual electrical angle and is expressed as a percentage.

For the same full range output, a multiturn potentiometer will have better resolution than a single-turn continuous-rotation unit.

LINEARITY/CONFORMITY—This parameter is one of the most important in the selection and application of a precision potentiometer. The terms *linearity* and *conformity* refer to the exactness of the relationship between the actual and the theoretical function characteristics. Generally, *linearity* refers to the straight-line relation of figure 2-6, while *conformity* refers to nonlinear relations such as sine, sine/cosine, and square function potentiometers and how the output "conforms" to the theoretical characteristic.

When a potentiometer is constructed with end taps, there is always some resistance that the wiper cannot move over. This resistance is called the *end resistance* and makes it impossible for the output voltage to reach either of the terminal voltages applied to the winding ends.

Figure 2-8 shows that the output voltage does not pass through either zero volts or E volts as is shown in the ideal curve of figure 2-6.

Figure 2-9 shows linearity specified in terms of the maximum deviation from the ideal curve; it is given as a percentage of the total applied voltage. The actual characteristic deviates from the ideal characteristic because of (1) the wire diameter not being constant, (2) unequal spacing of turns, (3) the turns not being identical in size, and (4) the resolution.

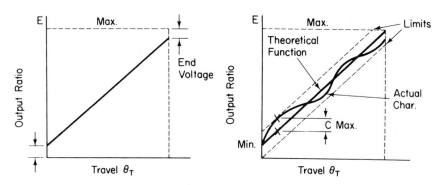

FIG. 2-8. Characteristic of Ideal Potentiometer with End Resistance

FIG. 2-9. Terminal-based Linearity

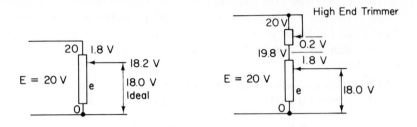

FIG. 2-10. Output Voltages with and without a High End Trimmer

The effects of end resistance can be nullified by using special potentiometers called "trimmers" which are connected to either or both ends of the function potentiometer. Figures 2-10 and 2-11 show two trimmers connected as high end and low end trimmers. These trimmer potentiometers can be adjusted to obtain $e = 0_{volts}$ with the wiper at $0°$ and $e = E_{volts}$ with the wiper at θ_t. If exact values of the end voltages are not important, then the trimmers may be adjusted to minimize the maximum deviation from the ideal characteristic.

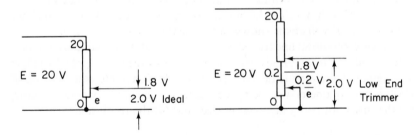

FIG. 2-11. Output Voltages with and without a Low End Trimmer

Figure 2-12 shows that the end voltages are exact, but a deviation in the characteristic does exist. Figure 2-13 shows that the deviation is minimized by the trimmers. However, this causes some deviation at each end and is called the *best straight line fit to the ideal*. When both trimmers are used, the specification is called *independent linearity*.

When it is only possible to trim at the high end, the specification is called *zero-based linearity*. Figure 2-14 shows this.

Conformity can also be improved by the use of trimmers. Therefore, it may be desirable to specify conformity in terms of (1) *terminal-based*, (2) *independent-based*, or (3) *zero-based*. Generally speaking, independent

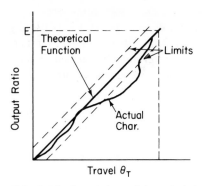

FIG. 2-12. Comparison of Actual and
Theoretical Function

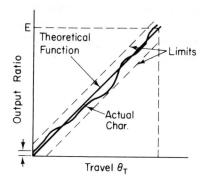

FIG. 2-13. Independent-based
Linearity

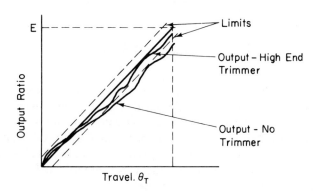

FIG. 2-14. Zero-based Linearity

linearity or conformity is the specification most often given by manufacturers.

RESISTANCE TOLERANCE—Standard tolerances are usually given as $\pm 5\%$, but they may go as low as $\pm 1\%$. The absolute value of the resistance is of minor interest because the output voltage is some proportion of the input voltage; the ratio is the important figure.

TAP LOCATION—Taps are made by a single weld to a single turn and are thus low in resistance and can be located quite accurately. The best practical tap tolerance can range from $\pm 0.1°$ up to $\pm 1.0°$. Tap location tolerance may have an effect on the accuracy of a potentiometer when it is used in a servo system, and it should be analyzed carefully.

POWER RATING—The wattage rating of precision potentiometers is not very large; generally, it is in the order of 1W to 10W, and it is usually specified at some particular ambient temperature. If the ambient temperature is greater than 60°C, then the potentiometer must be derated. Under this condition, the excitation voltage must be reduced. See figure 2-15.

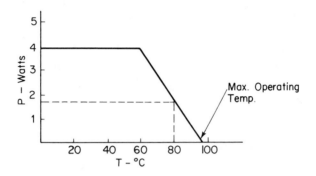

FIG. 2-15. Potentiometer Derating Curve

NOISE—Noise is defined as any spurious variation in the electrical output not present in the input. Generally speaking, it can be broken down into four forms: (1) *resolution* noise caused by voltage variation as the wiper moves from turn to turn; (2) *shorting* noise caused by the different number of turns short circuited by the wiper; (3) *loading* noise caused by a change in wiper-to-winding resistance as the wiper moves; and (4) *generated* noise caused by thermocouple effect, etc.

The noise parameter is quite often given in ohms; the value of 100 ohms/potentiometer is about the maximum. Of the four forms of noise, the effect of loading noise is the most pronounced because of the limitation it imposes on the maximum permissible rotation speed; the limit is in the neighborhood of 300 rpm.

STARTING AND RUNNING TORQUE—Starting torque of a precision potentiometer is in the order of one-fifth to one-ounce inch. After a potentiometer is moving, less torque is required to keep it moving. Thus it can be seen why precision ball bearings are used in servo mounts whereas bronze sleeve bearings are used in bushing mounts.

A larger number of turns results in a greater torque, if the same full range of shaft output is required.

MOMENT OF INERTIA—The moment of inertia of precision potentiometers is usually given in gram-centimeters. On multiturn units, this factor may have an appreciable effect on system's performance.

AC CHARACTERISTICS—As long as the windings are considered pure resistance, the mathematical relations are the same for either ac or dc circuits. However, many turns of fine wire on the mandrel lead to inductive and capacitive effects between turns and between the turns and the copper mandrel. On 60 or 400 hertz systems, a reactive load of megohms may result. Also shielded leads may be required between the potentiometer and the load. Therefore, when used on ac, potentiometers of the single-turn continuous-rotation type with lower winding resistance are preferred.

ELECTRICAL OVERTRAVEL—Figures 2-16 and 2-17 show the mechanical and electrical travel of a wire-wound potentiometer as well as the overtravels.

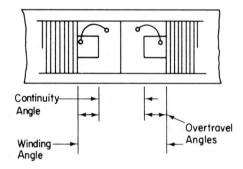

FIG. 2-16. Mechanical Overtravels and Heat Loops

The total mechanical travel is the travel of the shaft between specified stops. The stops are positioned so that the wiper comes to rest on the overtravels, except in continuous-rotation potentiometers. The electrical

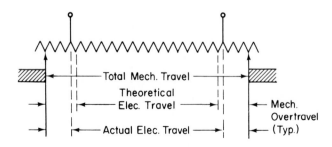

FIG. 2-17. Overtravel, Continuity, and Winding Angle

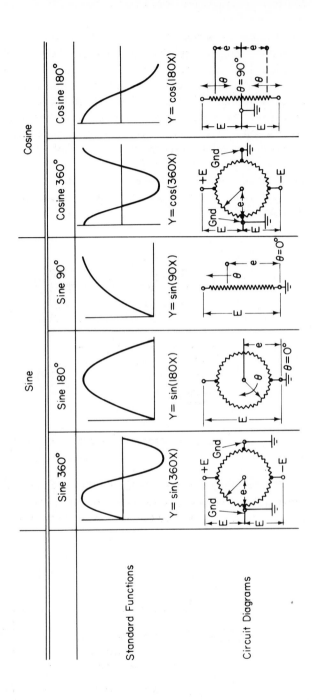

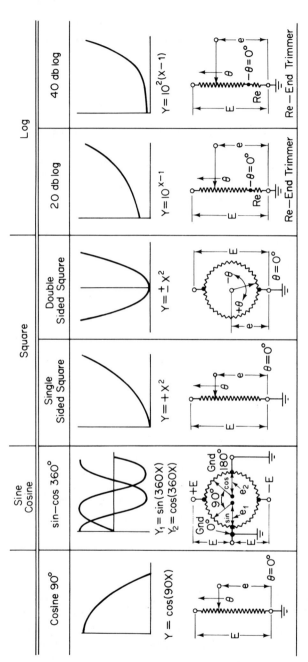

FIG. 2-18. Typical Resistance Functions for Non-linear Potentiometers (*Courtesy of Bourns Inc., Riverside, Calif.*)

23

winding angle is measured from the first to the last turn of the resistance element. The electrical continuity angle includes the winding angle and the overtravel angles.

2.8.   NONLINEAR FUNCTIONS

Many applications require functions that are not linear, functions such as a sine wave output, a cosine output, a log output, a square output. Most manufacturers can supply just about any function required or desired. See figure 2-18.

A nonlinear function can be achieved in a number of different ways (see figure 2-19) such as:

1. variable spacing of turns
2. change of wire size
3. change of wire type
4. contoured card mandrel
5. stepped card mandrel
6. square card mandrel

Some potentiometers have a large number of taps, and, by using external resistors, a variety of nonlinear functions can be obtained.

2.9.   NON-WIRE-WOUND POTENTIOMETERS

The strict definition of a *non-wire-wound precision potentiometer* is a potentiometer characterized by the continuous nature of the resistance element in the direction of wiper travel. To achieve this characteristic, the resistance element is made of a thick film of metal, carbon, or ceramic/ metal substance which is deposited on a nonconducting base. Such elements are continuous, noninductive, and offer a smooth path for wiper action.

These film potentiometers have a number of advantages over the wire-wound potentiometers, among which are: (1) wear and wiper bounce are kept very low; (2) higher wiper speeds can be utilized before continuity loss results, speeds to 2000 rpm; (3) failure of the resistance element is much lower; and (4) current surges very seldom cause element burnout. The most important advantage is that resolution is much improved.

Figure 2-20(a, b, c) shows the essential details of three different types of non-wire-wound potentiometers.

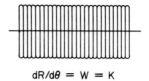

$$dR/d\theta = W = K$$

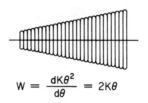

$$W = \frac{dK\theta^2}{d\theta} = 2K\theta$$

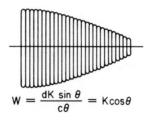

$$W = \frac{dK \sin \theta}{c\theta} = K\cos\theta$$

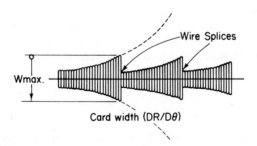

FIG. 2-19. Typical Card Shapes (*Courtesy of Bourns Inc., Riverside, Calif.*)

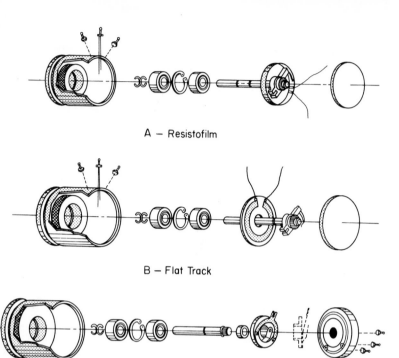

A — Resistofilm

B — Flat Track

C — Bulk Element

FIG. 2-20. Exploded Views of Non-wire-wound Potentiometers (*Courtesy of New England Instrument Co., Natick, Mass.*)

2.10. POTENTIOMETER CONNECTIONS

A potentiometer can be connected into a circuit in either of two ways. When connected as in figure 2-21, it is called *single-ended excitation* because one end of the winding is connected to ground. When connected as in figure 2-22(a) or (b), it is called *double-ended excitation* because either the center tap of the potentiometer is grounded or the center of the excitation voltage is at ground potential. The load is connected between the ground and the wiper.

2.11. OPERATION IN A SYSTEM

The potentiometer functions in a servo loop as a reference input element or a feedback element. In either case, it is used in making the conversion from mechanical position (shaft angle) to the electrical representation of this position.

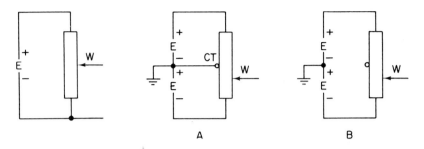

FIG. 2-21. Single-
ended Excitation

FIG. 2-22. Double-ended Excitation

A common connection for two potentiometers is that of a bridge circuit with the error voltage being measured between the two sliders, as is shown in figure 2-23(a). The diagram showing how the potentiometers might be shown in a block diagram is given in figure 2-23(b).

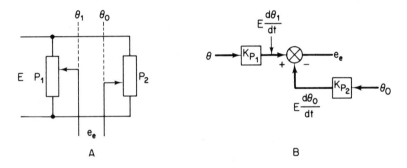

FIG. 2-23. A Potentiometer Error Channel and Block Diagram

POSITION FEEDBACK. Figure 2-24 shows the connection of a potentiometer used as a feedback element in a servo loop that controls mechanical position.

The servo motor, which is a two phase ac type, drives the wiper of the feedback potentiometer as well as the load. This output θ_0 is the assumed angular position of the load. The voltage taken from the wiper is the feedback voltage e_f, while the input voltage e_c taken from the reference potentiometer is the command which directs the loop to position the output shaft at a particular angle.

When e_c is larger than e_f, the error voltage e_e will have a certain polarity when it is fed to the ampl fier; conversely, when e_f is larger than

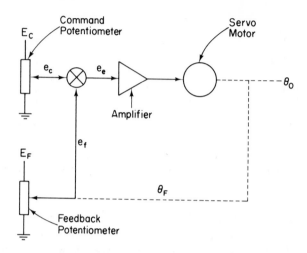

FIG. 2-24. Mechanical Position Servo with Potentiometer Transducers

e_c, e_e will be reversed in polarity. This reversal in polarity will cause the servo motor to drive in the correct direction in order to reduce the error voltage to zero. The loop is now at the null position.

This loop is capable only of accepting positive input voltage and driving toward positive values of θ_0. If it is desired to have the loop respond to negative signals and to drive toward a negative angle, then a double-ended circuit must be used.

If E_c in figure 2-24 is held at a constant value and E_f, the feedback source, is made variable, then the computation of a reciprocal results.

MULTIPLICATION.   Figure 2-25 shows the connection of a potentiometer used to provide multiplication of two inputs with one input being variable and one being constant. As the mathematics shows, this multiplication also uses division by a constant.

2.12. ZEROING A POTENTIOMETER

In testing or using a potentiometer, care must be taken to ensure that the dial or pointer position at zero degrees gives the correct voltage (resistance) output that results from the particular potentiometer. This output voltage will vary from zero to a finite value depending on whether the potentiometer is a single-turn limited-rotation or continuous-rotation potentiometer of all types and/or functions.

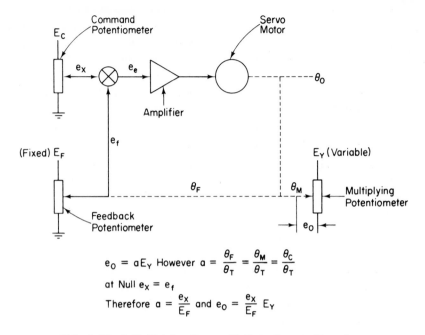

$$e_O = aE_Y \text{ However } a = \frac{\theta_F}{\theta_T} = \frac{\theta_M}{\theta_T} = \frac{\theta_C}{\theta_T}$$

at Null $e_x = e_f$

Therefore $a = \dfrac{e_x}{E_F}$ and $e_O = \dfrac{e_x}{E_F} E_Y$

FIG. 2-25. A Multiplying Servo with Potentiometer Transducers

A potentiometer may be checked with a high impedance ohmmeter in order to measure output or function resistance. A low voltage may be applied across the two fixed end points (never apply voltage between a fixed end and a tap) and the output voltage(s) read. If the output voltage is incorrect, then the pointer or dial may be loosened and rotated and then clamped in the correct position. In some cases, depending on the mounting, the body of the potentiometer may be rotated while the pointer or dial is held; it is then clamped in the new position.

PROBLEMS

1. Two potentiometers of 50K ohms each are connected across 110V dc as an error detector. Determine the following:
   (a) the wiring diagram, (b) the relative position of the wipers to give an error voltage of 40V if they are single-turn, (c) three-turn, (d) ten-turn.

2. Two 4W potentiometers of unknown resistance with 360° electrical travel are connected across 60V ac as an error detector. A voltmeter

between the slider indicates a voltage of 48V. The reference potentiometer is set at 310°. What is the position of the feedback or follow potentiometer? What are their resistances? Sketch the ac wave at each potentiometer slider when an error voltage of 48V exists. Sketch the wave when the error voltage is driven to zero.

3. A potentiometer is designated as 360° sine. What does this mean? Sketch the output wave that could be obtained.

4. A potentiometer is designated as 180° sine/cosine. What does this mean? Sketch the output wave shapes.

5. A tangent function potentiometer is being used in a servo. If 30V dc is impressed across the potentiometer, determine the slider voltage for angles of 45°, 60°, 75°, 90°, 180°, 270°, 315°, 360°. Plot the output. Hint:

$$\text{Let } E_0 = \frac{\tan (75°\text{X})E}{(\tan 75°)(2)}; \qquad X = \frac{\theta_0}{\theta_t}$$

6. A wire-wound potentiometer has an electrical rotation of 3590°. It has 4800 turns. What is the theoretical resolution?

7. A three-turn wire-wound potentiometer has 2100 turns of wire on its mandrel. What is the theoretical resolution?

8. Potentiometer resistance elements are sometimes made of conductive films applied to glass plates. This is done in order to: (a) increase resolution, (b) increase linearity, (c) increase power handling ability, (d) reduce friction. Which answer is correct and why?

9. If the brush connections to a sine/cosine potentiometer are reversed, what will happen to the output voltages?

10. A 5K potentiometer having 350° of total travel is loaded with a 6K load resistor. If the applied voltage is 15V, what is the theoretical voltage supplied across the load at 125° of slider movement?

11. (a) In the circuit of problem 10, prove that when the 6K potentiometer is removed and the resistance between slider and ground is called R_x, the output voltage will be:

$$V_0 = E \frac{R_x}{R_p}$$

(b) Prove that after replacing the 6K load, the output voltage will be:

$$V_0 = \frac{E \dfrac{R_x R_L}{R_x + R_L}}{R_p - R_x + \dfrac{R_x R_L}{R_x R_L}}$$

12. What is the difference between voltage resolution and angular resolution?

13. What is meant by the term linearity?

14. What is the difference between linearity and conformity?

15. Explain the difference between winding angle and continuity angle.

16. Give one advantage and one disadvantage of a multiturn potentiometer as compared to a single-turn potentiometer.

17. Explain the difference between terminal linearity and independent linearity.

18. What are trimmer potentiometers and why are they used?

19. The following diagram shows a servo loop with a feedback potentiometer. (a) Prove that the equation is correct. (b) Recopy the diagram and mark on it (1) where the error voltage would be found, if and when it exists, and (2) where the feedback voltage is found.

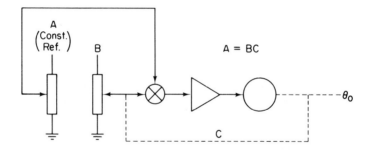

20. Two three-turn potentiometers of 10K ohms are connected across 36V dc as an error detector. Three turns of the potentiometers correspond to 352° of mechanical movement. Find the wiper position of the feedback potentiometer to give an error voltage of 18.8V if the command potentiometer is set at 94°.

21. On a small aircraft landing field, the shaft that the wind sock is mounted on is connected mechanically to the shaft of a sine/cosine potentiometer. The potentiometer is excited from 50V ac. Determine the wind direction if the readouts of the x and y coordinates are −23.8V and 44.4V respectively.

22. The wattage rating of single-turn potentiometers that have theoretical electrical angles of 354° and resistances of 20K ohms is 5W for wire wound and 2.5W for plastic for temperatures up to 85°C. At 150°, the wattage rating is zero. Determine the wattage that each of the potentiometers can handle if they are used at an ambient temperature of 110°C.

THREE

Variable reluctance transducers

3.1. INTRODUCTION

Another type of transducer is the variable reluctance magnetic type in which the magnetic reluctance of a transformer is changed by changing either the position of the secondary coil in respect to the primary or the position of the iron core in respect to the coils. The three most common devices that utilize this principle are the E-core transformer, the linear variable differential transformer (LVDT), and the microsyn. The first two sense changes in position along a straight line path; the microsyn senses change in angular position.

3.2. PRINCIPLE OF OPERATION

The basic principle underlying the operation of any of these transducers is that the ac magnetic coupling between two or more coils can be changed simply by changing their relative mechanical position or by changing the position of a separate moveable core.

E-CORE TRANSFORMER. The E-core transformer has a magnetic circuit that has an I and E core as shown in figure 3-1.

There are three windings wound around the E-core. The center leg winding is the primary. The two windings on the outside legs are the secondaries and they are connected in series so that their voltages oppose each other. In the exact zero position, the reluctance of the magnetic path

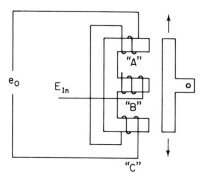

FIG. 3-1. Schematic of an E-core Transformer

through both cores is the same; thus, the voltages induced in coils A and C are equal and opposite, and hence the output voltage, e_0, is zero. When a change in system position causes the I-core to move, the reluctance changes, and the voltages induced in coils A and C change. When the voltage in coil A is larger than in coil C, the I-core has moved toward A and away from C. If the core is moved toward C and away from A, then the voltage across C will be larger than across A. In either case, the net voltage across the output terminals is different from zero, depending on the offset. In the first case, the phase of the output voltage is the same as the phase of the voltage across A; in the second case, it is the same phase as the voltage across C. Thus, the amplitude of the output voltage gives a magnitude indication of the core displacement, and the phase of the output voltage indicates the direction of the displacement.

LINEAR VARIABLE DIFFERENTIAL TRANSFORMER.   The LVDT is the most commonly used variable reluctance element. Figure 3-2 shows its principal parts.

A primary coil is wound around the center portion of the form, and two identical secondaries are wound around each end of the form. A magnetic core rod is located inside this coil assembly. The secondary coils are connected externally in a series-opposing circuit. The motion of the magnetic core will vary the mutual inductance of each secondary to the primary which, in turn, will vary the voltage induced in each secondary.

If the core is in the exact center between the secondary coils, then the voltage induced in each coil will be the same and 180° out of phase with the other so that there will be zero output voltage. This is the null position.

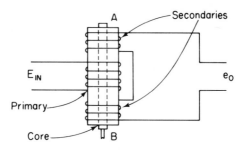

FIG. 3-2. Schematic Diagram of a Linear Variable Differential
Transformer

When the core is moved from this null position, the voltage induced
in the secondary coil toward which the core is moved will increase, and
the voltage induced in the other secondary will decrease. This produces a
differential voltage output that varies in a linear manner with the core
position. If the core is moved the other way, the output voltage would be
shifted in phase by 180°. When voltage is plotted against core position,
within the range of linearity or just beyond, the graph is a straight line
going through the origin and lying in quadrants I and III. When voltage
is plotted as a positive quantity, regardless of phase, the graph is V-shaped.
See figures 3-3 and 3-4.

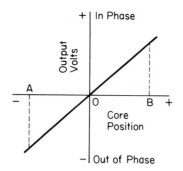

FIG. 3-3. Output Voltage and Its
Phase Reference

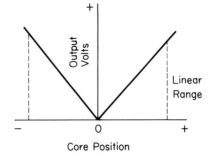

FIG. 3-4. Absolute Magnitude of
Output Voltage

DC OPERATED LVDT.   The LVDT just described works on ac and, to a
certain extent, is the workhorse of the reluctance transducers. However,
the advent of microelectronic circuitry and the simplicity of dc operation

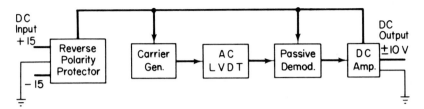

FIG. 3-5. Block Diagram of a DC-LVDT

has led to the design and construction of the DC-LVDT. The heart of this device is still an AC-LVDT, but now electronic circuits have been added; this is shown in the block diagram of figure 3-5.

The diagram shows that the module contains a complete passive demodulator/dc amplifier signal conditioner.

The full-scale output voltage does not depend on the dc input as it does in an AC-LVDT. Thus the term "sensitivity" which describes the output of an AC-LVDT cannot be used to describe the DC-LVDT. Instead, the output scale factor is specified in volts per inch of core travel or in millivolts per mil.

ROTARY VARIABLE DIFFERENTIAL TRANSFORMER. The differential transformer used for measuring angular displacement is known as the Rotary Variable Differential Transformer (RVDT); it is shown in figure 3-6.

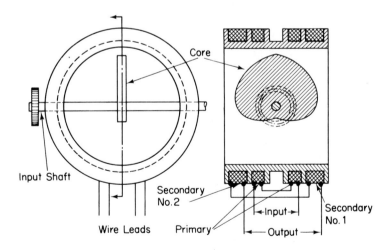

FIG. 3-6. Simplified Cross-section of an RVDT (*Courtesy of Schaevitz Engineering, Camden, N.J.*)

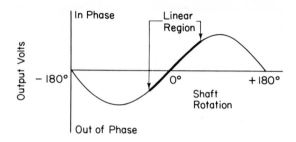

FIG. 3-7. Output Characteristics of an RVDT

Note the difference in the core designs of the RVDT and the LVDT. The RVDT uses a heart-shaped core of magnetic material with the shape determining the linear output range of the element over its specified range of rotation. While most RVDT's allow a full 360° of rotation, only about ±40° to ±60° of rotation are used for the useful output (see figure 3-7). However, the latest designs have extended this linear range to as much as ±340°. The output of these later units increases linearly to a maximum at 340° and then drops nonlinearly to zero volts.

The RVDT is available in both ac and dc types; dc units contain integral thick film signal conditioning, as is shown in figure 3-8.

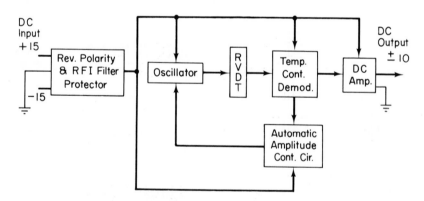

FIG. 3-8. Electronic Block Diagram of an RVDT

3.3.   USE IN SERVO SYSTEMS

The excellent linear output characteristic of an LVDT or RVDT makes these devices extremely useful as null-position transducers in

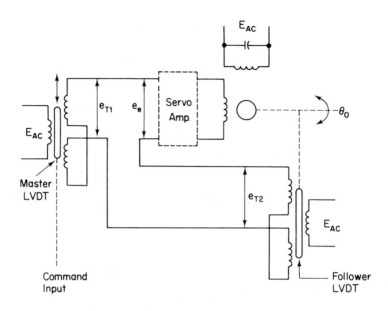

FIG. 3-9. Null Balance System

follow-up servo systems. A *follow-up servo system* maintains a fixed positional relationship between two or more moveable members. If the command member changes position, then the servo system moves the feedback or "slave" members in a manner that restores their positions relative to the command. Figure 3-9 is a representative schematic wiring diagram of such a system.

Electrically, the system works as follows. At null, the two LVDT cores are at the same position; consequently, their output voltages are equal and 180° out of phase so that the error voltage, e_e, is zero with the motor at rest. If the core position of the command LVDT is moved in an upward direction, the magnetic coupling between the secondary coils will change so that e_{T1} increases in a positive direction. This voltage, e_{T1}, thus becomes larger than e_{T2}, and an error voltage, e_e, appears at the input to the amplifier. This error voltage is amplified and fed to the control phase of the two-phase servo motor so that the motor starts and runs in the direction of rotation that will drive the core of the following LVDT until it matches the core position of the command LVDT. At this point, the error voltage is again zero, and the motor stops. Conversely, when the command LVDT is moved in the reverse direction, reverse motor action will take place.

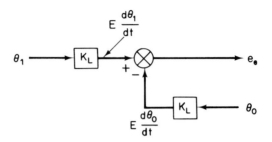

FIG. 3-10. Block Diagram of an LVDT Error Channel

A diagram showing how the two LVDT's might be shown in a block diagram is displayed in figure 3-10.

3.5.   ZEROING AN LVDT

An LVDT should be mounted on a support that is free from vibrations and that is a safe distance away from any strong magnetic fields that may emanate from other power transformers, motors, relays, contactors, etc.

In terms of zero, the LVDT armature should be in the exact center of its coil. If the electrical zero output does not agree with the mechanical shaft zero position, then the following adjustments can be made:

1. For fine adjustments, the zero-adjusting screw is rotated until the servo shaft reaches its zero position.

2. For large adjustments above 2% of the total range, the flexure plate is adjusted by the zero-adjusting screw until the plate is in a vertical position. The coil is then physically moved until the servo shaft nears its zero position, and it is then locked in place.

3. If an LVDT is being used by itself, then the armature core can be held at exact zero as given by the output voltage, and the body of the transformer moved until this is reached. The body is then clamped in place.

3.6.   THE MICROSYN

The microsyn is a reluctance type transducer that is used when the angular movement being controlled is only a few degrees. It is an inductive device that has primary and secondary windings wound on poles.

Two poles, 180° apart in mechanical space, comprise the primary, and two poles, also 180° apart, comprise the secondary. The rotor is a bar of low reluctance iron with no windings. Figure 3-11 shows the rotor in the zero position; the flux paths are indicated by the dotted lines. In this position, the turns of the output windings are not cut by flux created by the exciting current; therefore, there is no voltage induced in the secondary windings. When the rotor is moved away from the zero position in the clockwise direction, an emf of a certain magnitude (depending on displacement) and phase will be induced in the secondary windings, and an output voltage will result. When the rotor is turned in the opposite direction, the magnitude of the voltage will again be determined by the displacement, but it will now be of opposite phase. The microsyn can be constructed so that it has excellent resolution and is extremely linear. It may also be wound to give a number of functional forms.

In addition to its application as a generator of an electrical signal, the microsyn may also be used as a torque transmitter when the torque is proportional to the product of two currents. The windings are now called

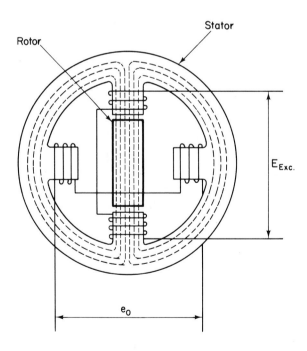

FIG. 3-11. Elementary Microsyn

the *reference* and *control* winding rather than primary and secondary. The amount of torque is determined by the magnitude of the currents; the direction in which the torque acts is determined by their phase relation, or polarity. Since torque is the principal thing here, transformer action does not enter in; therefore, the exciting currents can be either ac or dc.

FOUR

Resolvers

4.1. GENERAL

An induction resolver is essentially a transformer with a rotary electromagnetic coupling between the primary and secondary windings. The windings are located on the stator and rotor in such a manner that the output voltage has an amplitude which is proportional to the sine or cosine of the input shaft position. In normal operation, the resolver stator, which is similar to a transformer primary, is excited with alternating voltage. The coupling between the rotor and the stator is magnetic, the same as between the primary and secondary of a transformer. In a resolver, however, the position of the rotor can be changed with respect to the stator; this allows the magnetic coupling to vary with shaft rotation. This variable coupling produces an output voltage which has an amplitude that is equal to the stator voltage multiplied by the sine or cosine of the rotor shaft's angular position with respect to the stator. See figures 4-1 and 4-2.

FIG. 4-1. Two-winding Resolver

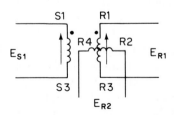

FIG. 4-2. Three-winding Resolver

4.2.   FOUR-WINDING RESOLVER

To make induction resolvers even more useful, two windings are
provided on both the stator and the rotor. The pairs of windings are
located at right angles to each other. Complex trigonometric functions
involving both sines and cosines can be solved when both stators are
excited. The voltage transformation ratio from primary to secondary is
usually 1:1, although other values are used. Other windings may be
added for feedback or compensation in order to achieve greater accuracy
and to make the resolver less sensitive to environmental variations and
load and source impedance variations. See figure 4-3.

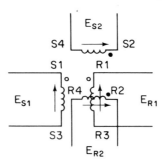

FIG. 4-3. Four-winding Resolver

The flux created by E_{s1} induces a voltage in R1-R3 that is determined
by the cosine of the angle whereas the flux created by E_{s2} induces a voltage
in this same coil that is determined by the sine of the angle.

Figure 4-4(a) depicts two stator windings at right angles to each
other. Assume that each winding is excited with 10V ac. Each winding
will have a magnetic field of its own which will be at a right angle to the
other. The resultant of these fluxes will be at 45° and equivalent to 14.14V.
However, this flux vector may assume any position depending on the
amplitude and polarities of the exciting currents; its angular position is
equal to the arc tangent of the ratio of the two stator currents.

Figure 4-4(b) shows the same stator windings with one rotor winding
at a right angle to one stator and parallel to the other stator. The output
voltage of this winding is then 10V.

When two rotor windings are used as in figure 4-4(c), the voltages are
proportional to the magnitude of the flux vector and to the sine or cosine
of the angle of rotation of the rotor winding with respect to the vector.

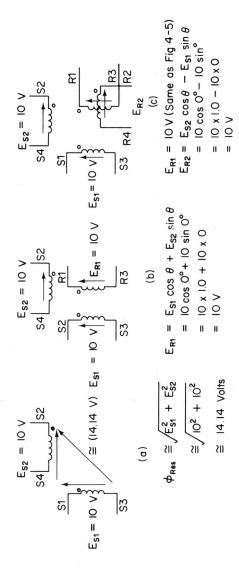

$$\phi_{Res} \cong \sqrt{E_{S1}^2 + E_{S2}^2}$$
$$\cong \sqrt{10^2 + 10^2}$$
$$\cong 14.14 \text{ Volts}$$

(a)

$$E_{R1} = E_{S1} \cos\theta + E_{S2} \sin\theta$$
$$= 10 \cos 0° + 10 \sin 0°$$
$$= 10 \times 1.0 + 10 \times 0$$
$$= 10 \text{ V}$$

(b)

$E_{R1} = 10 \text{ V}$ (Same as Fig 4-5)

$$E_{R2} = E_{S2} \cos\theta - E_{S1} \sin\theta$$
$$= 10 \cos 0° - 10 \sin 0°$$
$$= 10 \times 1.0 - 10 \times 0$$
$$= 10 \text{ V}$$

(c)

FIG. 4-4. Induced Coil Voltages of a Resolver

43

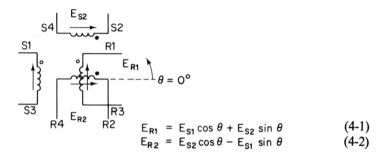

$$E_{R1} = E_{S1} \cos \theta + E_{S2} \sin \theta \qquad (4\text{-}1)$$
$$E_{R2} = E_{S2} \cos \theta - E_{S1} \sin \theta \qquad (4\text{-}2)$$

FIG. 4-5. Basic Schematic of a Four-coil Resolver at
Electrical Zero

4.3. ELECTRICAL ZERO

The most important application factor is the *electrical zero* and the corresponding electrical relations as referred to the resolver terminals. Figure 4-5 shows a four-coil resolver with fixed primaries (stators) and rotating secondaries (rotor). The relative phase of the windings is shown by the polarity dots; the polarity of the voltage is analogous to the direction of the voltage vector. For the zero position, stator coil 1, S1-S3, induces maximum voltage in rotor coil 1, R1-R3, but zero voltage in rotor coil 2, R2-R4. Similarly, S2-S4 induces maximum voltage in R2-R4 but zero in R1-R3. Equations 4-1 and 4-2 give the voltages.

Standard rotation for positive values of shaft angle θ is counterclockwise (CCW). As the shaft is turned CCW from zero, each stator winding induces voltages in both rotor windings. These voltages vary in magnitude and phase (direction) in accord with the sine-cosine relations in each quadrant. Figure 4-6 shows a rotor angle of 45°. The phase of the

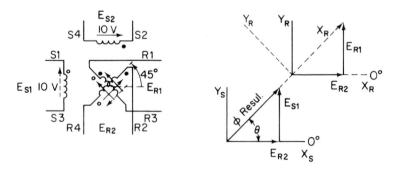

FIG. 4-6. Determination of In-phase and Out-of-phase Voltages for a Rotor
Position of 45°

voltages induced in the rotor windings, as a result of the current flowing in the S2-S4 winding, is indicated by black dots. Both the voltages at R1 and R2 are in phase with the voltage at S2 because both the sine and cosine of 45° are positive. The phase of the voltage induced in the rotor windings, as a result of the current flowing in the S1-S3 winding, is indicated by open circles. The voltage at R2 is in phase with the voltage at S1 whereas the voltage at R4 is out of phase with the voltage at S1 because the cosine of 45° is positive while the sine of $-45°$ is negative.

4.4.   RESOLUTION

Of the basic resolver computations—resolution, composition, and transformation of axes—resolution is the simplest and is used to convert the polar coordinates of a vector to rectangular coordinates (see figure 4-7). A vector $R \angle \theta$ can be "resolved" into two components, x and y, because $x = R \cos \theta$ and $y = R \sin \theta$.

The electrical inputs to the servo loop of figure 4-7 are R and θ; the loop operates as a potentiometer follow-up system which converts electrical input, θ, to the corresponding angular shaft position, θ_0, of the resolver. The exciting voltage applied to the stator winding is converted to the required rectangular coordinates.

4.5.   COMPOSITION

Composition converts two rectangular coordinates to their corresponding polar coordinates. It is the inverse of resolution and always requires a servo loop with a servo motor and amplifier (see figure 4-8).

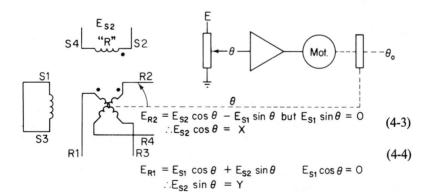

$$E_{R2} = E_{S2} \cos \theta - E_{S1} \sin \theta \text{ but } E_{S1} \sin \theta = 0$$
$$\therefore E_{S2} \cos \theta = X \tag{4-3}$$

$$\tag{4-4}$$

$$E_{R1} = E_{S1} \cos \theta + E_{S2} \sin \theta \quad E_{S1} \cos \theta = 0$$
$$\therefore E_{S2} \sin \theta = Y$$

FIG. 4-7. Resolution—Converting a Polar Coordinate to its Rectangular Component

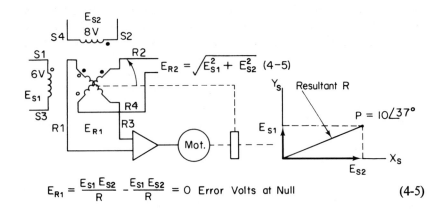

$$E_{R1} = \frac{E_{S1} E_{S2}}{R} - \frac{E_{S1} E_{S2}}{R} = 0 \;\; \text{Error Volts at Null} \qquad (4\text{-}5)$$

FIG. 4-8. Composition—Converting Two Rectangular Coordinates to a Polar Coordinate

The inputs E_{S1} = y and E_{S2} = x are applied to the two stator windings, and the outputs are taken from the two rotor windings. The voltages E_{S1} and E_{S2} form a resultant magnetic flux vector which lies at the angle θ to the x-axis.

This magnetic flux vector induces voltages in R1-R3 and R2-R4. The R2-R4 output is applied to the amplifier in the proper phase in order to drive the motor and the resolver shaft CCW for positive angles of θ. The servo motor turns the shaft through the angle θ until the null is reached; this occurs when the R1-R3-axis is at right angles to the flux vector; the voltage applied to the amplifier then becomes zero. The R2-R4-axis is then parallel to the flux vector, and maximum voltage appears across the R2-R4 terminals. The voltage at R1-R3 is the error voltage in the servo loop, the voltage at R2-R4 is the resultant R, and the dial indication is the desired angle θ.

4.6. ROTATION OF COORDINATE AXES

Many ships, aircraft, and space vehicles require information generated in one coordinate system to be converted into another coordinate system. For example, components of velocity measured with an inertial navigator must be converted into aircraft pitch-and-roll velocities. Thus, rectangular coordinates from one set of axes must be rotated to a second set of axes that are at some angle relative to the first. Another example would be the problem of converting data in terms of a ship's heading into data in terms of true North in order to furnish target latitude and longitude data to

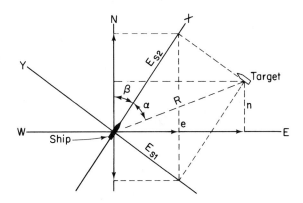

FIG. 4-9. Latitude and Longitude of a Target

other ships in the fleet. The course the ship is on is called the *relative-bearing coordinates* with North being called the *true-bearing coordinates*. See figure 4-9.

Voltages proportional to relative-bearing coordinates x and y are applied to the respective stator windings of a resolver; thereby producing a resultant magnetic flux vector. The rotor windings are then rotated from their zero position through an angle equal to the course angle of the ship from North. The voltages induced in each rotor winding are proportional to the sine or cosine of its angular position with respect to the flux vector, not with respect to zero. If the reference is made with respect to zero, then the outputs are found from equations 4-1 and 4-2. The following two examples are used to illustrate the steps necessary in finding the true-bearing coordinates.

EXAMPLE 4-1

See figure 4-10. Six volts (representing an *x*-coordinate of $+6$) and 8V (representing a *y*-coordinate of -8) are applied to primaries S2-S4 and S1-S3 respectively; the course angle is 37° NNE. The coordinate $y = -8$ is represented by a phase reversal of S1-S3; thus, the resultant magnetic field lies in the fourth quadrant. The rotor windings are now rotated through an angle of 37°; therefore, the voltage induced in each is proportional to the component of the resultant field which lies parallel to the axis of the rotor winding R1-R3. The voltage induced in R2-R4 is zero because its axis is at right angles to the resultant field. The true bearing coordinates are $x = 0$ and $y = -10$, and the target is located 10 units due South of the ship.

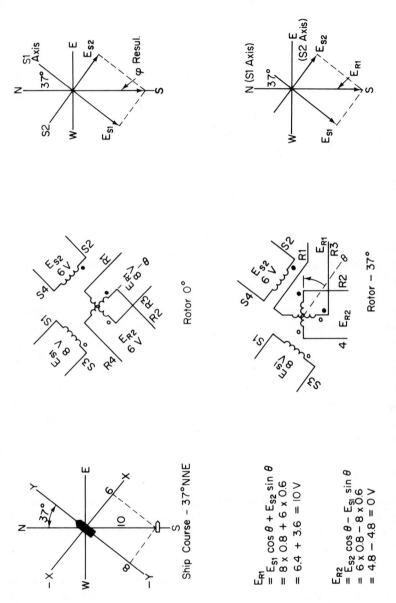

Ship Course – 37°NNE

E_{R1}
$= E_{S1} \cos \theta + E_{S2} \sin \theta$
$= 8 \times 0.8 + 6 \times 0.6$
$= 6.4 + 3.6 = 10\text{V}$

E_{R2}
$= E_{S2} \cos \theta - E_{S1} \sin \theta$
$= 6 \times 0.8 - 8 \times 0.6$
$= 4.8 - 4.8 = 0\text{V}$

Rotor 0°

Rotor – 37°

FIG. 4-10. Conversion of Relative Bearing Coordinates to True Bearing Coordinates

EXAMPLE 4-2

The radar on an aircraft carrier picks up the blip of an enemy ship and supplies the distance and angle that the carrier is from the target. Other ships in the fleet must be informed of the true-bearing coordinates so that they can converge on the target. The carrier is steaming on course on a relative-bearing axis (x-axis) which lies 20° NNE of true North. The enemy ship is 36 miles from the carrier and at an angle of 50° NNW from it. Determine:

1. the wiring diagram
2. the relative-bearing coordinates
3. the true-bearing coordinates

Solutions

(1)

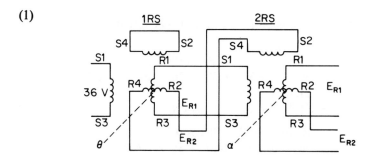

(2) Using the resolver equations 4-1 and 4-2, we will solve for E_{R1} and E_{R2} of 1RS which will be the x- and y-(relative-bearing) coordinates.

$$E_{R1} = E_{S1} \cos \theta + E_{S2} \sin \theta$$
$$= 36 \cos 50°$$
$$= 36 \times 0.643$$
$$= 23.3V \text{ or } 23.3 \text{ miles}$$

$$E_{R2} = E_{S2} \cos \theta - E_{S1} \sin \theta$$
$$= 0 - 36 \sin 50°$$
$$= -36 \times 0.765$$
$$= -27.6V \text{ or } 27.6 \text{ miles}$$

NOTE: The negative sign indicates an out-of-phase ac relationship only; it has no bearing on the solution.

(3) E_{R1} and E_{R2} found in step 2 are the excitation voltages E_{S1} and E_{S2} respectively for 1RS. Again, using equations 4-1 and 4-2 except using angle alpha, ∂, rather than theta, θ, we will solve for E_{R1} and E_{R2} of 2RS which will be the north and west (true-bearing) coordinates.

$$
\begin{aligned}
\text{N:} \quad E_{R1} &= E_{S1} \cos \partial + E_{S2} \sin \partial \\
&= 23.3 \cos 20° + 27.6 \sin 20° \\
&= 23.3 \times 0.940 + 27.6 \times 0.343 \\
&= 21.9 + 9.47 \\
&= 31.36\text{V or } 31.36 \text{ miles } \textsc{north}
\end{aligned}
$$

$$
\begin{aligned}
\text{W:} \quad E_{R2} &= E_{S2} \cos \partial - E_{S1} \sin \partial \\
&= 27.6 \cos 20° - 23.3 \sin 20° \\
&= 27.6 \times 0.940 - 23.3 \times -0.343 \\
&= 25.94 - 7.99 \\
&= 17.95\text{V or } 17.95 \text{ miles } \textsc{west}
\end{aligned}
$$

The north and west coordinates may also be found from

$$
\begin{aligned}
\text{N} &= \text{R} \cos \theta \cos \partial + \text{R} \sin \theta \sin \partial \\
&= 36 \times 0.643 \times 0.94 + 36 \times 0.765 \times 0.343 \\
&= 21.76 + 9.45 \\
&= 31.21\text{V or } 31.21 \text{ miles Ck.}
\end{aligned}
$$

$$
\begin{aligned}
\text{W} &= \text{R} \sin \theta \cos \partial - \text{R} \cos \theta \sin \partial \\
&= 36 \times 0.765 \times 0.94 - 36 \times 0.653 \times 0.343 \\
&= 25.89 - 7.94 \\
&= 17.95\text{V or } 17.95 \text{ miles Ck.}
\end{aligned}
$$

$\text{R} \cos \theta \cos \partial + \text{R} \sin \theta \sin \partial$ may be reduced as a trigonometric identity to $\text{R}(\cos \theta \cos \partial + \sin \theta \sin \partial)$ and then to $\text{R} \cos (\theta - \partial)$. $\text{R} \sin \theta \cos \partial - \text{R} \cos \theta \sin \partial$ may be reduced to $\text{R}(\sin \theta \cos \partial - \cos \theta \sin \partial)$ and then to $\text{R} \sin (\theta - \partial)$; therefore

$$
\begin{aligned}
\text{N} &= 36 \cos (50° - 20°) \\
&= 36 \cos 30° \\
&= 36 \times 0.866 \\
&= 31.2\text{V or } 31.2 \text{ miles Ck.}
\end{aligned}
$$

$$
\begin{aligned}
\text{W} &= 36 \sin (50° - 20°) \\
&= 36 \times 0.5 \\
&= 18\text{V or } 18 \text{ miles Ck.}
\end{aligned}
$$

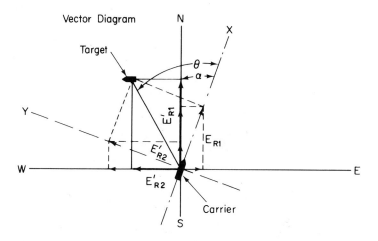

4.7. DATA TRANSMISSION— ANGULAR ADDITION/SUBTRACTION

Figure 4-11 illustrates the use of two resolvers in cascade to give angular addition or subtraction. Data, in the form of angular shaft positions, are transmitted from one place to another without any mechanical connections. Only one of the stator windings is used with the other winding being short-circuited. Figure 4-11 shows that the two resolver rotors are displaced 30° from their zero position. Ten volts is applied to S2-S4 of resolver No. 1. The voltage induced in R2-R4 is 8.66V, and this in turn is applied to S2-S4 of resolver No. 2. The 5V induced in R1-R3 of No. 1 is fed to the S1-S3 winding of No. 2. The voltages induced in windings R1-R3 and R2-R4 of No. 2 add, giving 8.66V and 5V respectively. These values represent the sine and cosine of 60° which is the sum, 30° + 30°, of the two resolver rotor angles.

Figure 4-12 shows angular subtraction where the same angular and voltage values are assumed. The difference between figures 4-11 and 4-12 is that the connections to S2-S4 of No. 2 have been reversed. The resultant voltages are therefore 0V and 10V, respectively, which represent the sine and cosine of 0°, (30° − 30°).

When the output E_{R1} of resolver No. 2 in figure 4-12 is applied to an amplifier, and the amplifier output is in turn fed to a servo motor, a servo loop, where one resolver follows another, will be obtained. As an example, let $E_{S2} = 10V$, $\theta = 40°$ (resolver No. 1), and $\alpha = 30°$ (angular position of resolver No. 2). Before the servo loop starts to operate, the voltage output of R2-R4 of 2RS will be 9.85V, and the voltage output of R1-R3

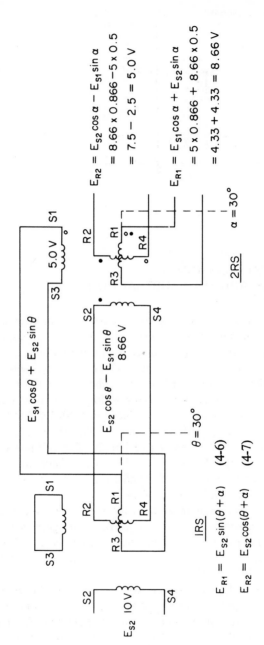

FIG. 4-11. Resolver Schematic Showing Electrical Data Addition

$E_{R1} = E_{S2} \sin(\theta + \alpha)$ (4-6)

$E_{R2} = E_{S2} \cos(\theta + \alpha)$ (4-7)

$\underline{1RS}$

$\theta = 30°$

$E_{S2} \cos\theta - E_{S1} \sin\theta$
8.66 V

$E_{S1}\cos\theta + E_{S2}\sin\theta$

5.0 V

$E_{R2} = E_{S2}\cos\alpha - E_{S1}\sin\alpha$
$= 8.66 \times 0.866 - 5 \times 0.5$
$= 7.5 - 2.5 = 5.0$ V

$E_{R1} = E_{S1}\cos\alpha + E_{S2}\sin\alpha$
$= 5 \times 0.866 + 8.66 \times 0.5$
$= 4.33 + 4.33 = 8.66$ V

$\underline{2RS}$ $\alpha = 30°$

E_{S2} 10 V

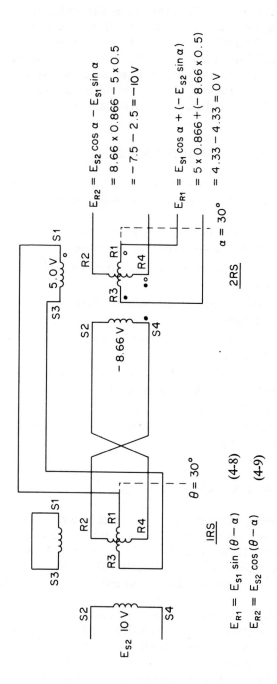

FIG. 4-12. Resolver Schematic Showing Electrical Data Subtraction

$E_{R1} = E_{S1} \sin (\theta - \alpha)$ (4-8)

$E_{R2} = E_{S2} \cos (\theta - \alpha)$ (4-9)

$\theta = 30°$

IRS

$\alpha = 30°$

2RS

$E_{R2} = E_{S2} \cos \alpha - E_{S1} \sin \alpha$

    $= 8.66 \times 0.866 - 5 \times 0.5$

    $= -7.5 - 2.5 = -10V$

$E_{R1} = E_{S1} \cos \alpha + (-E_{S2} \sin \alpha)$

    $= 5 \times 0.866 + (-8.66 \times 0.5)$

    $= 4.33 - 4.33 = 0V$

to the amplifier will be $-1.74V$. The minus sign indicates an out-of-phase voltage. The servo motor will then rotate in the correct direction, determined by the phase of E_{R1}, in order to drive the rotor of resolver No. 2 to the 30° position. At this point, the voltage to the amplifier will be zero, the motor will stop, and the data transmission will be $\theta - \alpha = 0$. In a circuit such as this, resolver No. 1 is the reference element, and resolver No. 2 is the feedback element and error detector.

4.8.   PERFORMANCE CHARACTERISTICS

The equations and examples shown are for an ideal resolver. The practical resolver differs from the ideal in the following respects:

1. Functional error—The output voltages that are induced are not exactly sine or cosine functions of the rotor angle.
2. Interaxis error—The voltages at the null positions are not zero but some small value.
3. Null output—Null voltage or quadrature voltage exists due to the quadrature component.
4. Transformation unbalance—The transformation ratio between the pairs of windings is not exactly 1:1.
5. Proportional voltage error—A deviation may exist between the actual mechanical shaft angle and the ideal position required to generate a perfect sine or cosine function.
6. Phase shift—A phase shift of the secondary voltage with respect to the primary voltage may occur.

4.9.   ZEROING A RESOLVER

In testing or using a resolver, great care must be used in the mechanical means used to position the rotor. On many units, a calibrated dividing head has proved to be the most satisfactory. The error in the head should be less than 30 seconds of a degree of angle. There may also be a line on the housing and a radial index line on the end of the shaft for the zero reference.

The procedure for zeroing is simply to connect one of the stator windings (Type A resolver) across rated voltage and then to measure the output voltages with a precision voltmeter. One rotor winding should show maximum voltage corresponding to the cosine of 0°, while the other should give zero voltage corresponding to the sine of 0°. If the voltages are not maximum or zero, then the housing of the resolver should be rotated, while the pointer is held at zero, until these conditions are achieved. Then the housing should be clamped in this position. Figure 4-13 shows the exploded view of a four-coil resolver.

PROBLEMS

1. An AC LVDT has the following data: input 6.3V, output 5.2V, range ±0.50 inches. Determine:
   (a) the wiring diagram with polarities
   (b) the plot of output voltage *vs.* core position for a core movement going from +0.45 inches to −0.30 inches
   (c) the output voltage when the core is −0.25 inches from center
   (d) whether this output voltage is in phase or out of phase

2. A four-coil resolver is used to convert slant range and elevation angle to horizontal range and height. Assume that one volt is proportional to 500 feet.
   (a) With 5V applied to stator winding S2-S4 and the rotor rotated at 20°, determine the horizontal range and height in volts and feet.
   (b) Repeat problem 2a for 18V excitation and 210° rotation.
   (c) Repeat problem 2a for 12V excitation and 320° rotation.

3. The resolver of problem 2 is used to convert horizontal range and height to slant range and elevation.
   (a) With 12V applied to S1-S3 and 18V applied to S2-S4, determine the slant range in volts and feet and the elevation angle.
   (b) Repeat problem 3a for 10V and 15V excitation.
   (c) Repeat problem 3a for 24V and 8V excitation.

4. For a resolver rectangular-to-polar transformation loop, assume x = 17V and y = 17V and that the output shaft is initially at 30°. What is the voltage applied to the amplifier? What is the null angle?

5. The radar on an aircraft carrier picks up the blip of an enemy ship and supplies the distance and angle that the carrier is from the target. Other ships in the fleet must be informed of the true-bearing co-ordinates so they can converge on the target. The carrier is steaming on course on the x-axis, which lies 40° NNE from true North. The radar indicated that the enemy ship is 42 miles away at an angle of 70° NNW. Determine:
   (a) the relative-bearing coordinates in volts and feet
   (b) the true-bearing coordinates in volts and feet
   (c) the vector diagram

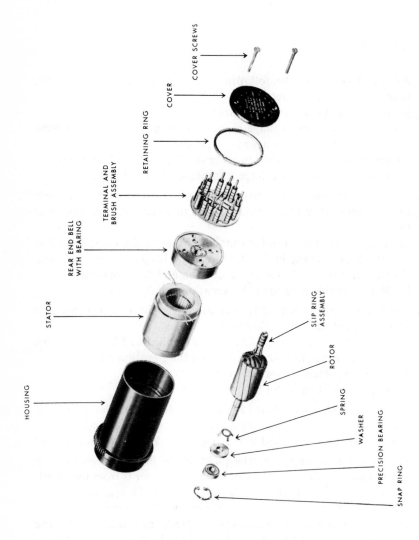

HOUSING

STATOR

REAR END BELL
WITH BEARING

TERMINAL AND
BRUSH ASSEMBLY

RETAINING RING

COVER

COVER SCREWS

SLIP RING
ASSEMBLY

ROTOR

SPRING

WASHER

PRECISION BEARING

SNAP RING

FIG. 4.13. Exploded View of a 4-coil Resolver (Reeves Instrument Corp.)

6. For a resolver data transmission loop, assuming $E_{S1} = 20V$, what is the voltage applied to the amplifier for the following conditions:
   (a) $\theta = 30°$, $\alpha = 26°$
   (b) $\theta = 30°$, $\alpha = 34°$

7. Two four-coil resolvers are used in a data transmission loop where the output voltages of the second resolver represent angular addition of the rotor positions. With 10V applied to stator windings S2-S4 of resolver 1, and the two rotors set at 30° and 40° respectively, determine:
   (a) the voltage applied to both stator windings of resolver 2
   (b) the output voltages of resolver 2
   (c) if angular addition is being accomplished; check by making a vector diagram

8. The connections from the rotor winding R2-R4 of resolver 1 to the stator winding of resolver 2 are reversed. With the same excitation voltage and rotor positions as in problem 1, determine:
   (a) the voltages applied to the stator winding of resolver 2
   (b) the output voltages of resolver 2
   (c) if angular subtraction is being accomplished; check by making a vector diagram

FIVE

Synchros

5.1. GENERAL

Synchros are electric machines that are widely used in modern control and signaling applications where it is often necessary to control the angular position of one shaft by positioning another shaft. They are used as an electrical means of transmitting shaft position information, even though a considerable distance may lie between the two shafts. The two shafts are tied together electrically in such a manner that when one is turned, the other will turn in exactly the same way or in a predicted way. There is no mechanical connection between the two shafts, and this represents the great advantage of the use of synchro devices.

The name *synchro* originated in the United States Navy, and it means a device that is "self-synchronous"; that is, they are "synchronous" with themselves. Other common names for the same machine are *selsyn*, *autosyn*, *teletorque*. The names *magnesyn* and *telegon*, however, are not to be confused with a synchro because their principle of operation is different. The different kinds of synchros can be classified approximately by size and accuracy as:

1. power synchros
2. instrument synchros
3. control and indicator synchros

Power synchros are really wound-rotor induction motors whose rotor voltages must be of the same value and whose rotors must operate at the same per unit speed. They may or may not have the same number

TABLE 5-1

Type	Nomenclature	Input(s)	Output(s)
Transmitter	Control—CX Torque—TX	Mech. Shaft Angle	Elec. Synchro Data
Receiver	CR TR	Elec. Synchro Data	Mech. Shaft Angle
Control Transformer	CT	1. Elec. Synchro Data 2. Mech. Shaft Angle	Error Voltage
Differential Transmitter	CDX TDX	1. Elec. Synchro Data 2. Mech. Shaft Angle	Elec. Synchro Data (Sum or Difference)
Differential	TDR	1. Elec. Synchro Data (A) 2. Elec. Synchro Data (B)	Mech. Shaft Angle (Sum or Difference)

of poles. However, their open-circuit rotor voltages must be the same so that their rotor voltages will match at any speed. Some examples of their use are:

1. operation of large valves

2. printing presses

3. kiln feeders

4. exact synchronism of the ends of a vertical lift bridge

Instrument synchros are usually extremely small and light. They are used only to carry a light-weight pointer to indicate position because they develop a very small torque. They are constructed like a miniature rotor-wound induction motor except that the rotor is generally wound for single-phase excitation and has two definite field poles.

Control and *indicator synchros* are constructed in the same manner as instrument synchros, although they may be smaller in size. Power and instrument synchros are usually not too accurate whereas control and indicator synchros have errors that are measured in tenths of degrees or less.

Table 5-1 presents the different synchros and their data in terms of input and output.

5.2. BASIC SYNCHRO SYSTEMS

Synchro systems can be divided roughly into two groups depending on whether they are used to give:

1. torque transmission, or

2. voltage indication

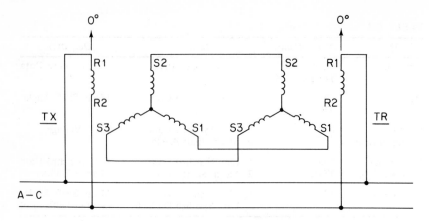

FIG. 5-1. Connections of a Torque Transmitter and Receiver

The first type of system is made up of two synchros between which torque is transmitted electrically in order to rotate the shaft of the motor or receiver synchro in synchronous position or correspondence with the shaft of the generator or transmitter synchro. The receiver shaft may carry a dial for indication purposes, or it may drive some other small mechanical device. A typical circuit is shown in figure 5-1.

The second type of system is also made up of two synchros connected together electrically in order to induce voltage in the synchro control transformer. This voltage has a polarity and a magnitude which are functions of the relative direction and amount of displacement between the shafts of the two synchros. This voltage can be used for indication purposes, but it is usually used as a control voltage for a much larger servomechanism system. A typical circuit is shown in figure 5-2.

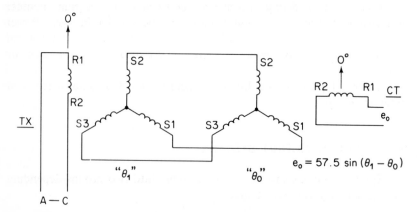

$$e_o = 57.5 \sin (\theta_1 - \theta_0)$$

FIG. 5-2. Connections of a Torque Transmitter and a Control Transformer

5.3. BASIC SYNCHRO THEORY

The rotor of a synchro is wound with a single-phase concentrated winding, and the stator is wound with three distributed windings that may be connected in either wye or delta to give poles 120° apart. Electrically, in normal operation, the synchro acts as a transformer, and voltages and currents in the unit are all single-phase. The rotor winding is excited by an ac source and by transformer action between the rotor and stator windings, voltages are induced in the three stator windings, the magnitude of these voltages depends on the angular position of the rotor with respect to the stator. These voltages are of line frequency, and they are in phase with the rotor voltage. The voltage in each coil of the stator varies sinusoidally with the angle of the rotor with respect to that coil.

The most common transformation ratio between the rotor and a stator coil is 2.2:1 step-down. Thus, with 115V across the rotor, there is a maximum of 52V across any one stator coil; this maximum occurs when the stator coil is aligned with the rotor. The stator voltage value for any rotor angle may be found by applying the formula:

$$E = 52 \cos \phi \qquad\qquad (5\text{-}1)$$

where E is the maximum voltage in any one stator coil, and ϕ is the angle between rotor and stator coil.

5.4. ELECTRICAL ZERO

In measuring the angular position of a synchro shaft, some point must be chosen as the reference or starting point. This reference is usually taken as being the position in which the axis of the rotor is lined up with the axis of the stator coil No. 2. Thus, the rotor position is described in terms of the number of degrees that the rotor is rotated away from this reference position. This reference point is called *electrical zero*. Under these conditions, the voltage between S1 and S3 must be zero, and the phase of the voltage at S2 must be the same as the phase of the voltage at R1 (see figure 5-3).

A synchro is, in effect, a transformer that has one coil which may be rotated through 360°. The magnetic field within the synchro may also be rotated through 360°. If an electromagnet is inserted in this field, and it is pivoted in such a manner that it is free to turn, then it will always tend to line up with the magnetic field. This is the basic principle underlying all synchro operation. In figure 5-3, the three stator coils are shown 120° apart. If S1 and S3 are tied together, and ac is impressed across S2 and

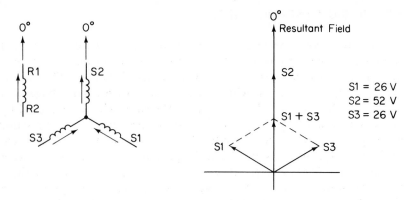

FIG. 5-3. Schematic and Resultant Fields for Electrical Zero

S3, then the field will be as is shown by the arrows. The rotor coil, if connected across ac, will now line up with the field of the stator and will stay in this position even though the alternating wave goes through its complete cycle. It is possible to get the rotor to change its position by 180°; this will be discussed later.

For the conditions shown in figure 5-3 with 115V across the rotor coil, there must be 78V measured between S2 and S3, also between S2 and S1, while zero volts is measured between S1 and S3. Thus, the resultant field is proportional to 78V and points at the zero degree position. The 78V figure comes about because the coil S2 is in phase with the rotor and has 52V induced in it; coils S1 and S3 meanwhile make an angle of 60° with the rotor and therefore have 26V induced in them. The vector sum is 78V.

In any particular synchro, these voltages in the electrical zero position are as indicated in figure 5-4, all are in phase with the rotor voltage. Figure 5-4(a) shows the voltage measured from S1 to S2 when the rotor is turned to any given angular position; figure 5-4(b) shows the voltage measured from S2 to S3; and figure 5-4(c) shows the voltage measured from S3 to S1. For the zero degree position, the voltages may be read in the following manner:

- The voltage from S1 to S2 equals 78 volts and is 180 degrees out of phase with the voltage from R1 to R2.
- S2 to S3 equals 78 volts; in phase with voltage from R1 to R2.
- S3 to S1 equals zero volts.

Voltages above the zero-axis are in the same phase as the rotor voltage R1-R2 while voltages below the zero axis are out of phase with

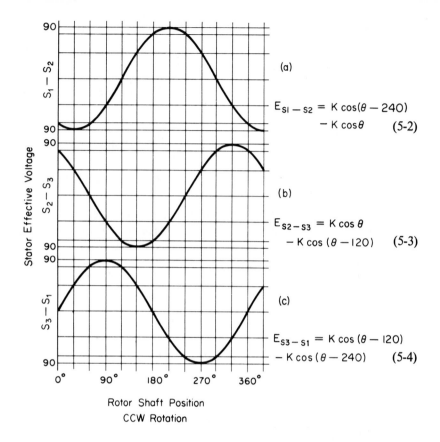

$$E_{S1-S2} = K\cos(\theta - 240) \quad (a)$$
$$- K\cos\theta \quad (5\text{-}2)$$

$$E_{S2-S3} = K\cos\theta \quad (b)$$
$$- K\cos(\theta - 120) \quad (5\text{-}3)$$

$$E_{S3-S1} = K\cos(\theta - 120) \quad (c)$$
$$- K\cos(\theta - 240) \quad (5\text{-}4)$$

FIG. 5-4. Phase Relationship of Voltages between Stator Terminals of a Synchro

rotor voltage R1-R2. The stator voltages are either in phase with the rotor voltage or 180° out of phase; no position in between exists. Thus, for a 90° CCW rotational position of the rotor, the voltage from S1 to S2 and from S2 to S3 must be half as large as the voltage from S3 to S1, and it must be 180° out of phase with voltage from R1 to R2 (counteracting the in-phase voltage of S3 to S1).

5.5. SUMMARY

The most important factor in analyzing synchro operation is the *resultant field* that is produced. Each stator coil produces a field of its own with a magnitude proportional to the voltage induced in it. The three stator fields then combine to form a resultant field with a fixed magnitude. To determine the direction of the resultant field, the following rules might be helpful.

1. In a transmitter, the field of any stator coil always opposes the field of a rotor coil; therefore, the resultant field in the stator always opposes the rotor field.
2. The resultant field in a receiver is in opposition to the resultant field of a transmitter stator (or in the same direction as the transmitter rotor field).
3. The field of a receiver rotor tends to line up in the same direction as the resultant field of the receiver stator.
4. When the rotor coils of a transmitter and receiver are lined up, the rotor coils induce equal and opposite voltages in their respective stator coils, thus causing the resultant fields to cancel. Therefore, no current flows between the two stators.

The fields of the coils in a stator, therefore, combine vectorially to produce a single field of a definite strength and in a definite direction. The movement of a receiver rotor occurs because the rotor's magnetic field aligns itself with the resultant stator field that is created. Thus, in any transmitter, the rotor and stator fields always oppose one another; however, in a receiver, they always aid one another.

5.6. HOW A RECEIVER FOLLOWS A TRANSMITTER

A fundamental circuit showing the electrical connections between a synchro transmitter and a receiver is illustrated in figure 5-1. Even though the distance between the units may be considerable, the rotor coils must be connected to the same single-phase supply source. If the transmitter rotor is set on the zero position, the stator voltage pattern will be that shown in figure 5-4. If the receiver is not on the zero position, then current will flow in the stator coils of the receiver, and its rotor, if free to turn, will line up with the zero position. Thus, the voltages induced in the two stator windings are equal and opposite to each other, and, therefore, no current will circulate in the windings.

If the transmitter shaft is turned to the 30° position, and the rotor of the receiver is momentarily held in its original zero position, then the voltage balance between the two stator windings is changed, and circulating currents will flow between the two windings. Figure 5-5 shows this voltage imbalance, and the current direction is indicated by the arrows.

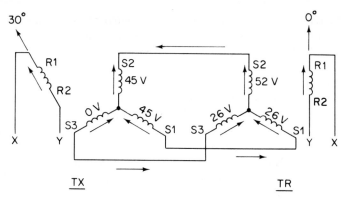

FIG. 5-5. Electrical Relations between a Transmitter and Receiver when
They Are at Different Mechanical Angles

This current flow produces a torque which tends to turn the rotor of the receiver to a position that is in alignment with the stator field. When alignment occurs, the voltages induced in the stator windings of the receiver are equal and opposite to the voltages induced in the stator windings of the transmitter.

It is important to realize that there is also a torque produced in the transmitter that is equal to that produced in the receiver if both synchros are not at the same shaft angle. If the transmitter is turned to 30° and then released before the receiver has "followed-up," the transmitter would be forced to turn backwards towards 0°, and the system would synchronize at an angle between 0° and 30°. This is the reason why the transmitter is generally not allowed to turn by itself but is held by the position of the input shaft.

5.7. SYNCHRO TORQUE

When a receiver is in correspondence with a transmitter, there is no torque being produced and no current circulating between the units. However, it is quite difficult to get the two to line up exactly without some lag of the receiver shaft behind the transmitter shaft. The smaller this lag is, the greater the *accuracy* of the system is. The rotors of two units in a typical system may line up with a misalignment of less than 0.5°. This misalignment is called the *angular error*. If the receiver is prevented from turning so that it cannot line up properly, a torque is produced which tends to turn the receiver rotor to the zero position. The currents creating this torque are large and will cause overheating if the misalignment is maintained.

The relationship between torque and angular error for any particular synchro unit is such that the torque increases to a maximum at an angular error of 90° and then decreases to zero at a shaft displacement of 180°. This 180° position is unstable because, if the displacement changes slightly in either direction, a torque will be produced which will quickly snap the rotor back to the zero position. This means that when the receiver is suddenly called upon to shift to a new position, it will have a tendency to hunt or oscillate. For this reason, a small, friction-driven flywheel is mounted on the receiver shaft to act as a damper. This also means that synchro units will always synchronize when their rotors are excited, and, from this, we can see why the system is called self-synchronous.

The torque of a synchro is given in terms of *torque gradient* which is a unit based on a 1° angular error. If the torque gradient is listed as 0.6 ounce-inch per degree, it would mean that a torque of 0.6 ounce-inch would pull the receiver rotor one degree away from the transmitter rotor. For small angles, the torque increases almost linearly. To keep the angular error as small as possible, the torque gradient is made as large as possible.

5.8. WIRING ERRORS

Since there are five interconnecting leads between a transmitter and a receiver, any reversal of connections or change in connections will have a material effect on the operation of the system as a whole. This may be desirable when it is necessary to have a fixed, angular displacement between the positions of the two shafts or when the direction of rotation should be opposite between the two shafts.

Reversal of the rotor leads will produce a 180° displacement of shafts, but the direction of rotation will remain the same. Reversing the rotor leads and reversing S1-S2 leads will produce 60° shaft displacement as well as a reversed direction of rotation. If the rotor leads are reversed back to their original connection, and S1-S2 leads remain reversed, then 240° shaft displacement and a reversed rotation will result. A cyclic interchange of stator connections (transmitter S1-S2, S2-S3, S3-S1) will produce 120° shaft displacement with direction of rotation remaining the same. Therefore:

1. Rotor Wiring Errors always introduce 180° mechanical shaft errors but with correct direction of rotation.
2. Stator Wiring Errors involving any pair of leads always give reversed direction of rotation; those involving S1-S2 or S2-S3 give 120° shaft

displacement as well; and those involving S1-S3 give no shaft displacement.

5.9. DIFFERENTIAL SYNCHRO

A *differential synchro* is a unit that is used to modify a basic synchro system. It may indicate the difference between the relative positions of two transmitter shafts; it may sum up the angular displacements of several shafts and represent the total as the displacement of one shaft; it may meter the rate of fuel flow in a multiengine plane; it may modify the angle between a transmitter and receiver shaft; or it may have any of a multitude of other uses.

A differential unit is constructed very much like a synchro transmitter except that the rotor has three sets of coils that are equally spaced and connected to produce poles 120° apart. Both stator and rotor windings have the same number of turns; therefore, the transformation between the corresponding stator and rotor coils is 1:1. This means that the differential, when the rotor is held in position, will have the same voltage at the rotor terminals as at the stator terminals. A differential thus can be constructed and connected to work as a differential transmitter or differential receiver.

If a differential transmitter is inserted between a transmitter and a receiver, and the rotor of the differential is not free to move, then the receiver rotor follows the transmitter rotor just as if the differential were not in the circuit.

Figure 5-6 illustrates the connections for a differential transmitter that is inserted between a transmitter and a receiver. Here, the transmitter rotor is held at zero position, and the differential rotor is turned to the 120° position. The maximum voltage is now induced in coil R1 of the differential rotor, and, since R1 is connected to S1 of the receiver stator, the resultant field is now in the direction of S1, and the receiver rotor turns clockwise to the 240° position. Therefore, the position of the receiver rotor is equal to the position of the transmitter minus that of the differential transmitter. Thus, the following rule holds true: TX − TDX = TR.

If one desires to add the position of the differential transmitter to that of the transmitter, then it is necessary to reverse the connections to S1-S3 and R1-R3 of the differential. If the circuit is analyzed, then the following rule can be proven: TX + TDX = TR.

If only the transmitter is reversed, that is S1-S3, the rule becomes: TX + TDX = −TR. If only the receiver connections S1-S3 are reversed, then the rule becomes: TX − TDX = −TR.

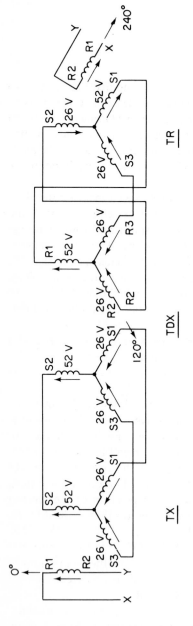

FIG. 5-6. Connections of a Torque Differential Transmitter that Will Give Subtraction

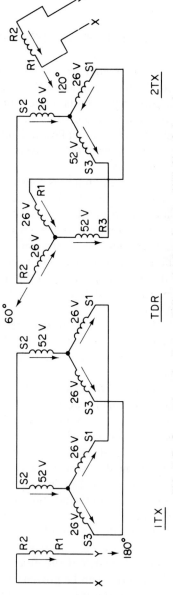

FIG. 5-7. Connection of a Torque Differential Receiver that Will Give Subtraction

A differential receiver is inserted between two transmitters in order to indicate the angle between their shafts. If there is no angular difference between the shafts of the two transmitters, then the shaft of the differential will be at the zero position. However, if the transmitters are set to two different angles, then the differential will indicate the difference between the two. This is illustrated by figure 5-7, which shows that 1TX − 2TX = TDR.

If one desires to get a minus TDR reading, then S1-S3 should be reversed for both transmitters so that 1TX − 2TX = −TDR. If one desires to add the two transmitter readings, then only R1-R3 of the differential need be reversed; under this condition, 1TX + 2TX = TDR. If only S1-S3 of the differential is reversed, then 1TX = 2TX = −TDR.

It can be seen that in either of the differential connections, a differential is not connected to the source of excitation; therefore, its exciting current must come from either of the standard synchros to which it is connected. It is normal practice to supply this excitation to the stator of the differential only, and this means that the synchro transmitter must be designed to carry this extra current. A specially designed unit, called a *synchro exciter*, is quite often used, and it may operate in the system either as a transmitter or as a receiver. In still other cases, balanced static capacitors are connected across the stator terminals of the differential unit. These capacitors have such a rating that the leading current they take is exactly equal to the lagging current of the differential stator winding. Thus, the synchro transmitter is required to furnish only the energy component of current, which is perhaps 10% of the total excitation current.

5.10. SYNCHRO CONTROL TRANSFORMER

A *synchro control transformer* is constructed very similarly to a differential unit except that it has a single rotor winding like a transmitter. It is used with a synchro transmitter as is shown in figure 5-2. The rotor winding is not connected to the supply source, and, under normal conditions, it carries no current. It is used to produce an output voltage that is proportional to the angular difference between the two shafts. This output voltage is called an *error voltage* because it exists only when the shafts are in "error" or misaligned.

If the shaft of the transmitter is set at zero position, then the magnetic field in the control transformer is in line with phase S2, and, if the shaft of the control transformer is turned to the zero position, then its winding axis will be at 90°, while the magnetic field and the output voltage will be at zero position. For any other position of the control transformer shaft,

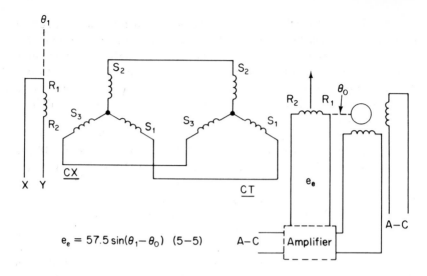

$$e_e = 57.5 \sin(\theta_1 - \theta_0) \quad (5\text{-}5)$$

FIG. 5-8. Connection of a Transmitter and Control Transformer with Amplifier and Servomotor

a voltage will be induced in the rotor coil that varies with the sine of the angle between the shafts. In the electrical zero position, coils S1 and S3 induce voltages in the rotor, but these voltages are equal and opposite in phase; therefore, the net result is zero.

When the rotor is turned so that it lines up with S2 (90° from zero position), the voltage induced in it will be a maximum of 57.5V. Rotating the shaft another 180° will again induce a maximum voltage but of opposite phase. Thus, the error voltage from a control transformer varies both in magnitude and in phase. The output voltage is thus given by $e_0 = 57.5 \sin (\theta_1 - \theta_0)$ with θ_1 being the transmitter position and θ_0 being the control transformer position. This makes the control transformer very useful in any system where position is being controlled. In these position control systems, the output voltage is normally fed into an electronic amplifier as an error signal. For this reason, the control transformer is quite often called an *error detector*. Figure 5-8 shows a circuit that controls the angular position of an output shaft. In this circuit, any change in input shaft position must be followed by a corresponding change in output shaft position.

The rotor of the synchro transmitter is mechanically connected to the input shaft. The rotor of the control transformer is mechanically connected to the output shaft. The electrical output of the control transformer rotor is fed into the input stage of a power amplifier. A two-phase ac control motor is used to furnish the mechanical power to rotate the output shaft and its associated load. The input to the control winding of the control motor is supplied by the amplifier. When the output shaft is in the correct position, the error voltage input to the amplifier is zero, and, therefore, there is no voltage impressed across the control winding of the control motor. Thus, the motor does not turn. If any change occurs in the input shaft position, then the control transformer generates an error voltage, and correction takes place to bring the output shaft into alignment with the input shaft. To operate satisfactorily, the amplifier must be phase-sensitive so that a change in either direction of rotation may be corrected for.

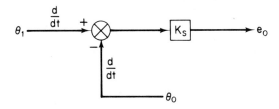

FIG. 5-9. Block Diagram of a Synchro Error
Channel

If one desires to have a dc control motor correct the angular discrepancy, then the output of the control transformer must be rectified in order to produce a proportional dc voltage that is also polarity sensitive.

A diagram showing how the CX and CT synchro pair might be shown on a block diagram is presented in figure 5-9.

5.11.   GEARED SYNCHRO SYSTEMS

When the rotors of synchro systems turn together at the same speed, the system is known as a *one-speed system*. However, due to internal friction and other errors in the system, an angular displacement, even at no-load, exists between the input and output shafts. This is called *no-load error*. If any external load is applied, then a load error of a greater magnitude arises. To achieve greater accuracy, geared systems called *double-* or *two-speed systems* are used. To understand why this is true, consider a synchro transmitter-receiver system used for data transmission. Suppose that 360° of rotation represent 1200 miles, and that the accuracy of the one-speed system is 15 minutes of a degree or 1 part in 1440. If an accuracy of 0.005% is required, then the error must be held to 0.06

mile. In order to achieve this accuracy, a 15X (15-speed) synchro pair could be used, thus

$$15 \text{ revolutions } = 1200 \text{ miles}$$
$$1 \text{ revolution } = 80 \text{ miles}$$
$$\frac{15 \times 80 \text{ miles } = 0.055 \text{ mile}}{60' \times 360°}$$

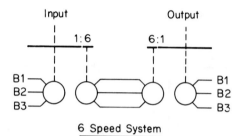

6 Speed System

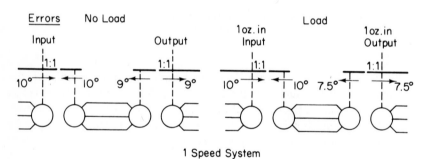

1 Speed System

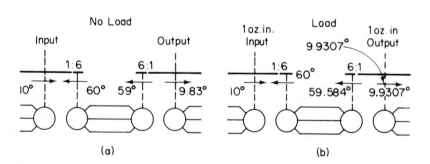

6 Speed System

FIG. 5-10. Comparison of Errors, No Load and Full Load, for a 1X versus a 6X System

The advantages of a double-speed system over a single-speed system can be easily seen in figure 5-10. Here, a comparison is made between the errors, no-load and full load, for a one-speed and a six-speed system. Internal frictions are such that an error of 1° can be considered as common to both systems under no-load conditions of figure 5-10(a). For the one-speed system, the output error will be 1° and for the six-speed system it will be 0.17°. This is a ratio of about 6:1 which shows that no-load errors are inversely proportional to the gear ratio.

Under load conditions of one ounce-inch of torque, the load error will be 2.5° for the one-speed system, and 0.0693° for the six-speed system. These load errors are found by assuming that the load torque is such that no-load errors can be considered zero and also that the torque gradient for the synchros is 0.4 ounce-inch per degree. With a 6:1 reduction twice between input and output, the load error in a double-speed system is inversely proportional to the square of the gear ratio.

5.12. SYNCHRONISM

In a single-speed system, self-synchronization is always achieved when power is turned on. However, in any geared system, there are the same number of positions of the output shaft where the receiver will align as there is in the number of the gear ratio. Thus, if the system for any reason is shut down, the receiver shaft may align in a different position. If a control transformer is used in place of a receiver, then there would be six different null output voltages; they would occur at 60°, 120°, 180°, 240° and 300° (multiples of 360°/6). The way to overcome these multiple nulls is to use two sets of transmitter-receivers or transmitter-control transformers. One pair is connected to controlled shafts, and the other pair is geared to run at the higher speed. *Coarse* error voltage is obtained from the former, *fine* information from the latter.

The principle of the double-speed system is demonstrated continually in one's wrist watch or the clock on the wall. The hour hand and minute hand give coarse and fine data respectively. In a similar manner, the coarse CX-CT pair prevents misalignment because it does not have multiple nulls, while the fine CX-CT pair increases accuracy.

The double-speed system shown in figure 5-10 has a one-speed (coarse) system in conjunction with a six-speed (fine) geared system. However, some device is required at the input to the amplifier which selects the data to be used in operating the servo motor, a device which measures the level of the coarse error. When this level is above a certain value, the coarse error signal is amplified and fed to the servo motor. When the coarse error signal drops below this value, the fine error signal controls the servo

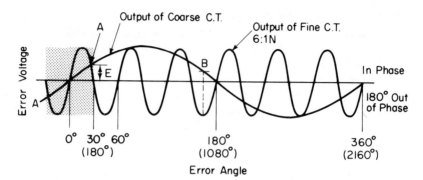

FIG. 5-11. Determination of Proper Switching Between 1X and 6X Synchros

motor. In selecting this error level, two criteria must be satisfied; they are:

1. The output shaft error must be less than one-half revolution of the fine synchro; otherwise, the fine error signal will cause the motor to be driven to an incorrect null position.

2. The level of the voltage applied to the motor should not change suddenly when switching occurs between signals; otherwise, an undesired transient effect will result. Both signals should be large enough to saturate the amplifier and to make it insensitive to signal changes.

Figure 5-11 shows the graph of the 6X and 1X synchro CT output voltages *vs.* output shaft positions. If the output shaft position is between 0° and 30°, then both voltages will cause positive rotation toward the commanded null position at zero. At 30°, the fine CT has rotated 30° × 6 or 180°. Beyond 30°, the fine CT has an output of opposite polarity, and, if it is applied to the servo motor, it would drive it away from zero. Therefore, control must be shifted to the coarse CT before the fine CT turns 180°. The shaded area shows the error angle over which the fine CT may be used. Outside this area, the coarse CT *must* take command. Thus, switching anywhere in this region will theoretically satisfy criteria 1. However, if switching takes place too close to 180°, the level of the fine signal might be too low to saturate the amplifier. In actuality, switching should be done at point A or thereabouts. The devices that are used to accomplish this switching are called *cross-over systems* or *synchronizers.* Relays or all electronic circuitry can be used to recognize the level of voltage at point A.

As the system approaches the 180° position of the coarse CT, its output voltage drops to a very low level, point B. An error angle this large

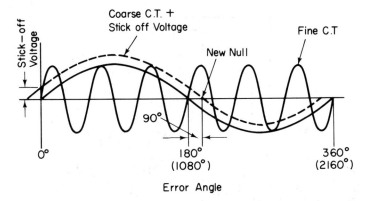

FIG. 5-12. Addition of a Stick-off Voltage to the Coarse CT Output

would permit the crossover system to deenergize and to shift control back
to the fine CT. However, at this point, the fine CT voltage is out of phase,
and thus the motor is driven to a false null at 180°. This always happens
when even gear ratios are used, unless something is done to prevent it.
Even so, even gear ratios are preferred over odd gear ratios. In order to
avoid this selection of an incorrect null, a voltage called a *stick-off* voltage
is added in series with the output of the coarse CT, as is shown in figure
5-12. The effect of this voltage, when added to the coarse voltage, is to
shift the two null positions of the coarse unit in opposite directions. Its
amplitude is selected so that the new coarse CT null occurs when the fine
CT completes an additional rotation of 90° past 180°.

To get the proper nulls at zero error angle, it is now necessary to rezero the coarse CT so that it produces a null once again at zero degree
shaft position. The new alignment of the coarse and fine nulls is shown in
figure 5-13; both CT's now have the same phase polarity at each null.

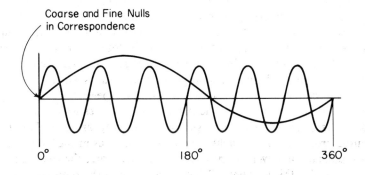

FIG. 5-13. Correlating Coarse and Fine Nulls Using a Stick-off Voltage

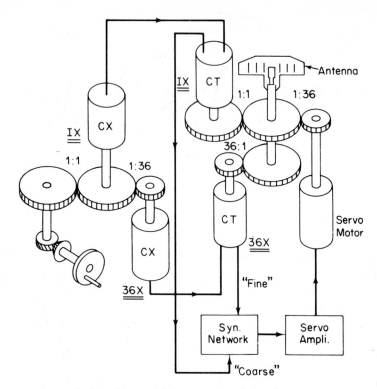

FIG. 5-14. Double Speed Transmission System

Figure 5-14 shows a 36:1 speed system that is used by the United States Navy to control antenna positions.

To achieve even greater accuracy, the gear trains could be eliminated so that gear inaccuracies will not impose a limit on total system accuracy. For example, a modern gear train has an error of around 2 minutes of angle, while CX and CT synchros are now available with less than 2 minutes of error; thus, the gear train governs the total error. If the mechanical gear train could be replaced with electrical gearing, then the total error could be reduced. The use of multipole synchros does exactly this.

When multipole synchros are used in two-speed systems, the gear inaccuracies are replaced with the synchro inaccuracies which include any errors caused by the electrical gearing, and they are included in the manufacturer's specified synchro error. Inaccuracies in the range of 5 to 10 arc seconds or lower are now available; therefore, the overall system accuracy is also this amount. Other advantages of the multipole synchro are its driving torque, size, and shape.

5.13. THE NEED FOR ADJUSTMENT

In order for synchros or any other transducers to work together properly, it is necessary that they be correctly connected and aligned to each other and to the other devices with which they are used.

Electrical zero is the reference point for aligning all synchro units. The mechanical reference point for any devices connected to the synchros depends on the particular application. For example, on board ship where course data are being checked, the reference would be true North. On a gun director servo, the reference could be a specific distance or an angle. No matter what the system, the mechanical and electrical zeroes must coincide.

The best way to accomplish this alignment is to align all synchros to electrical zero. The major advantage here is that if wiring errors occur, the trouble in the system will show up in the same way. Sometimes, a synchro can be zeroed by adjusting it mechanically by physically turning the synchro rotor or stator.

A synchro transmitter is on electrical zero when rated voltage on the rotor winding, R1 and R2, will induce no voltage between S1 and S3, and when the rotor and stator voltages subtract if R1 is connected to S2.

A synchro control transformer is on electrical zero when rated voltage connected between S1-S3 and S2 induces no voltage in the rotor, and when the rotor and stator voltages subtract if R1 is connected to S1.

A differential transmitter is on electrical zero when rated voltage connected between S1-S3 and S2 induces no voltage between R1 and R3 of the rotor, and when the rotor and stator voltages subtract if R2 is connected to S2.

5.14. ZEROING PROCEDURES

There are a number of methods that may be used to find electrical zero, but two major steps should be used. The two steps are a coarse or approximate setting and a fine setting. The coarse setting may be accomplished by a physical adjustment because the frame may have an arrow stamped on it, and a line may be engraved on the shaft end. When these line up, coarse adjustment is made. If these marks are not on the synchro, then an electrical test must be made.

5.15. ZEROING A TRANSMITTER— TX AND CX WITH A VOLTMETER

When rated voltage is applied to R1 and R2 as shown in figure 5-15(a) and a VTVM is connected between S1 and S3, the voltmeter should

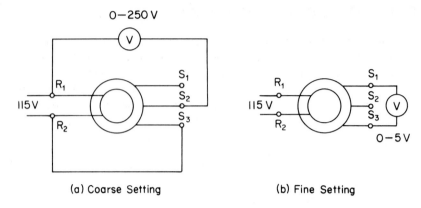

(a) Coarse Setting   (b) Fine Setting

FIG. 5-15. Electrically Zeroing a Transmitter

read zero or minimum when the synchro is at the zero position. However, a zero or minimum voltage will also result at 180°, unless the phasing between the rotor and stator voltages is carefully checked. Therefore, proceed in the following manner:

1. Connect the synchro and voltmeter as shown in figure 5-15.
2. Turn the rotor or stator until the meter reads a minimum voltage, about 40V. This is the coarse setting. See figure 5-15(a).
3. Reconnect the synchro and meter as shown in figure 5-15(b). Adjust the rotor or stator for a null or minimum reading of less than 1.0V. This is the fine setting, and the synchro can be clamped at this position.

5.16. ZEROING A RECEIVER— TR AND CR BY ELECTRICAL LOCK

Remove all connections and reconnect as illustrated in figure 5-16. The shaft and pointer will turn to 0°. Set the dial or pointer at this exact zero position. The voltage applied to R1-R2 should be 0.866 of the source voltage because this is the normal voltage induced in S2-S3 at 0°. If 78V is not available, then 115V may be used for only a few seconds because higher than rated voltage causes the synchro to overheat.

If the rotor is not free to turn, then a receiver can be zeroed in a manner similar to that used for zeroing a transmitter.

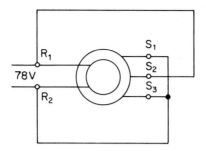

FIG. 5-16. Zeroing a Receiver by Electrical
Lock

5.17. ZEROING A CONTROL TRANSFORMER— CT USING A VOLTMETER

1. Connect the control transformer and voltmeter as shown in figure 5-17(a).

2. Turn the rotor or stator to obtain a minimum voltage reading; this will be the coarse setting.

3. Reconnect the voltmeter as shown in figure 5-17(b) and adjust the rotor or stator for the null or minimum voltage. Clamp the CT in this position.

5.18. ZEROING A DIFFERENTIAL TRANSMITTER— TDX USING A VOLTMETER

1. Connect the differential transmitter and voltmeter as shown in figure 5-18(a).

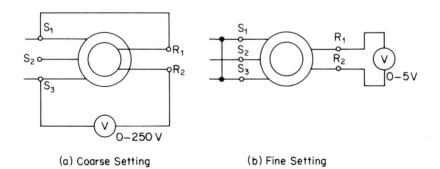

(a) Coarse Setting   (b) Fine Setting

FIG. 5-17. Electrically Zeroing a Control Transformer

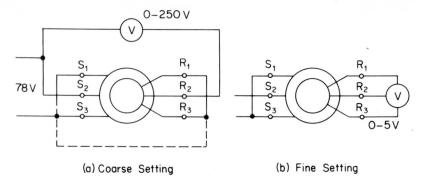

(a) Coarse Setting   (b) Fine Setting

FIG. 5-18. Electrically Zeroing a Differential Transmitter

2. Unclamp the differential and turn it until the meter gives minimum reading. This is the approximate zero.

3. Reconnect the unit as shown in figure 5-18(b) and turn the differential until a null reading is obtained. This is the fine zero setting.

PROBLEMS

1. A transmitter is at zero degrees; the voltage from R1 to R2 must be in phase with the voltage from: (a) S2 to S3, (b) S1 to S2, (c) S1 to S3, (d) the common point to S2. Why?

2. A receiver has its shaft in the 0° or 180° position when the axis of the rotor coil lines up with the: (a) axis of stator coil S2, (b) axis of stator coil S1, (c) axis of stator coil S3, (d) midway between the axis of coils S2 and S3. Why?

3. A synchro system is a: (a) single-phase system, (b) three-phase system, (c) two-phase system. Why?

4. Maximum current flows in the stator coils of a receiver when its rotor position: (a) is the same as that of the transmitter, (b) differs from the transmitter by 180°, (c) differs from the transmitter by 90°, (d) is displaced by 120° from the transmitter. Why?

5. When the shaft of a transmitter is set at the 120° position, the voltage measured between S1 to S3 will be: (a) 78V, (b) 52V, (c) 26V. Why?

6. Determine the voltage measured between each pair of stator leads of a transmitter for the following shaft positions: (a) 25°, (b) 150°, (c) 240°, (d) 330°.

7. A transmitter and receiver are zeroed properly and are then connected together in straight cyclic connection. Rotate the transmitter shaft to 180° and, at the same time, hold the receiver shaft at the 90° position. Make up a schematic diagram of the connections showing the stator coil voltages for both units.

8. Allow the shaft of the receiver in problem 7 to come into alignment with the shaft of the transmitter and then make up a schematic diagram of the connections showing the stator voltages for both units.

For Problems 9 through 16 use Magnetic Field Analysis as proof.

9. A transmitter and a receiver are connected together with S1 and S3 reversed at the receiver. If the transmitter shaft is turned to 335°, the receiver shaft will indicate: (a) 25°, (b) 155°, (c) 335°, (d) 215°. Prove your answer by a schematic diagram, also show the original starting position.

10. A transmitter is connected to a receiver in the following manner: S1-S2, S2-S1, S3-S3, R1-R1, and R2-R2. If the transmitter is turned to 240°, find (a) the position of the receiver, and (b) the starting position.

11. A transmitter is connected to a receiver in the following manner: S1-S1, S2-S3, S3-S2, R1-R2, and R2-R1. The transmitter is set at 60°, find the position of the receiver.

12. Repeat problem 10 except reverse the rotor connections to the receiver.

13. A differential transmitter is inserted between a transmitter and a receiver. The transmitter stator is connected to the differential stator in the following manner: S1-S3, S2-S2, and S3-S1. The differential rotor is connected to the receiver stator in the following manner: R1-S3, R2-R2, and R3-S1. The rotors of the transmitter and receiver are connected R1-R1 and R2-R2. Determine the position of the receiver if the transmitter is set at 90°, and the differential is set at 150°.

14. A transmitter is connected to a differential transmitter in the following manner: S1-S3, S2-S2, and S3-S1. The differential in turn is connected to a receiver by R1-S1, R2-S2, and R3-S3. The rotors of the transmitter and receiver are connected R1-R1 and R2-R2. Determine the position of the receiver if the transmitter is set at 50°, and the differential is set at 80°.

15. A transmitter is connected to a differential transmitter in the following manner: S1-S1, S2-S2, and S3-S3. The differential in turn is connected to a receiver by R1-S1, R2-S2, and R3-S3. The rotors of the

transmitter and receiver are connected R1-R1 and R2-R2. Determine the position of the receiver if the transmitter is set at 130°, and the differential is set at 30°.

16. Two transmitters are connected to a differential receiver in cyclic fashion. Determine the reading of the receiver when 1TX reads 135° and 2TX reads 75°.

.17. The axis of the rotor in a synchro control transformer when the zero position is: (a) at right angles to the axis of S2, (b) lined up with the axis of S1, (c) lined up with the axis of S2, (d) lined up with the axis of S3. Why?

18. A transmitter, control transformer, servo amplifier and servo motor are connected as an instrument servomechanism. Assuming that the transmitter is set at zero degrees, determine the input voltage to the amplifier for the following cases and indicate which voltages are out of phase:
(a) Transmitter input to 50°
(b) Transmitter input to −135°
(c) Transmitter input to 210°
(d) Transmitter input to −210°
(e) Transmitter input to −60°

19. A 24-speed geared synchro system has a no-load error of 1.75°. What is the error at the output?

20. What is the relationship between the gear ratio and the load error in a geared 24-speed system? Assume that the load error is 1.6°.

SIX

Mathematics of block diagrams

6.1. GENERAL

The purpose of a block diagram in any system, whether it be electrical, mechanical, hydraulic, pneumatic, chemical, etc., is to simplify the knowledge of the operation of the total system by conveying a better understanding of the relationship of the various parts. Only essential details are shown in order to give functional operation of all elements within the total system. The block diagram is combined with the transfer function of each element in the system to give a clear picture of the input and output signals. The *transfer function* which is defined as the ratio of the output signal to the input signal is placed within the block representing each element.

The techniques used in transforming and/or reducing block diagrams from very complicated structures to a single block are based on the use of a few identities and algebraic rules. To assist in performing the required algebra, other definitions of symbols concerning block diagrams need to be made. These symbols are:

1. The *block* represents the transfer function of the system element.

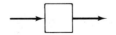

2. The *summing junction* represents the place where addition or subtraction of different signals is done.

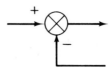

3. The *take-off* points represent the places where more than one input or output signal is used.

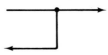

4. The *directional arrows* represent the flow of the signal.

The identities and other short cuts used in simplifying complex block diagrams are shown in the following pages and examples.

6.2. DIAGRAM MATHEMATICS

An open-loop control system that has a gain of G is shown by the block diagram depicted in figure 6-1.

A closed-loop system that has a gain of G is shown by the block diagram depicted in figure 6-2. Figure 6-2(a) shows the feedback to be unity or 1.0, while figure 6-2(b) shows a feedback factor of H which can be varied.

In equations 6-2 and 6-3 when the denominator has a plus sign, we know that the feedback voltage, e_f, subtracts from the reference or input voltage, e_1 and gives *negative feedback*. Negative feedback always gives stable system operation with the following four characteristics: (1) gain is reduced, (2) stability is increased, (3) response time is slowed down, and (4) bandwidth is increased. Negative feedback is the foundation upon which all automatic control is built; it is illustrated graphically by figures 9-2, 9-3(b, c, d).

On the other hand, when the denominator has a minus sign, we know

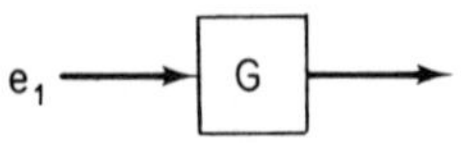

$$e_1 \longrightarrow \boxed{G} \longrightarrow e_0 \quad e_0 = Ge_1 \quad \frac{e_0}{e_1} = G \text{ (Open Loop Gain)} \quad (6\text{-}1)$$

FIG. 6-1. Open-loop Diagram and Gain

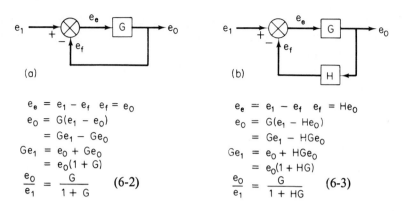

FIG. 6-2. Derivation of System Gain for Closed-loop Systems

that the feedback voltage, e_f, adds to the reference or input voltage, e_1 and gives *positive feedback*. Positive feedback leads to unstable system operation because, as the resultant denominator approaches zero, the oscillations become larger and larger. When the open-loop gain, G or HG, equals unity, the system becomes a pure oscillator because overall gain is infinite. This is shown by curve A in figures 9-3 and 9-4. What is actually happening is that the feedback signal strengthens the error signal so that the actual error is compounded to the point where the system saturates, and considerable damage may result to any rotating components and/or other devices. Positive feedback has the following characteristics: (1) very high gain (up to infinity), (2) very unstable, (3) extremely fast response time (digital in nature), and (4) a very narrow bandwidth. Positive feedback is alright in some electronic devices, but it is not used in automatic control systems.

The systems of figures 6-2(a) and 6-2(b) can now be represented by single blocks. See figures 6-3(a) and 6-3(b).

The open-loop gain in the system that is shown in figure 6-3 is equal to G or HG. This gain may be used to determine the steady-state frequency response of a closed-loop system using the *open-loop transfer function*. A transfer function allows the various elements of a servo system to be changed in block form for the purposes of simplifying or

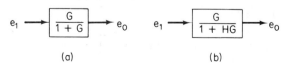

FIG. 6-3. Simplified Block Diagrams of the Closed-loop
Systems of Fig. 6-2

reducing. The transfer function may be considered an *operator* because it operates on the input to give an output. With the use of a number of different rules, given in figure 6-4, blocks may be combined into a single block, a pick-off point or a summation junction may be shifted ahead of or behind blocks, all for the purpose of diagram reduction.

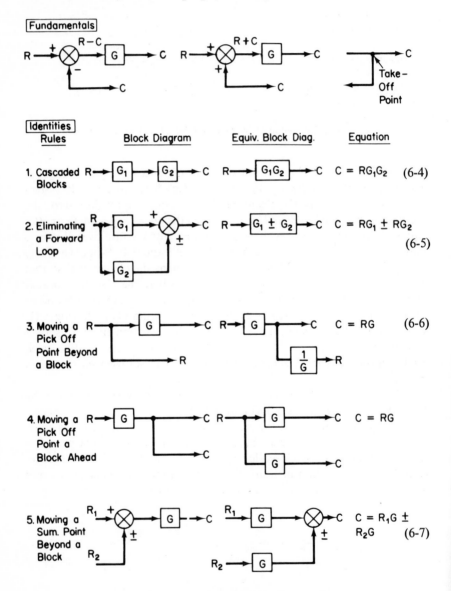

FIG. 6-4. Basic Block Diagram Manipulations

| Rules | Block Diagram | Equiv. Block Diag. | Equation |

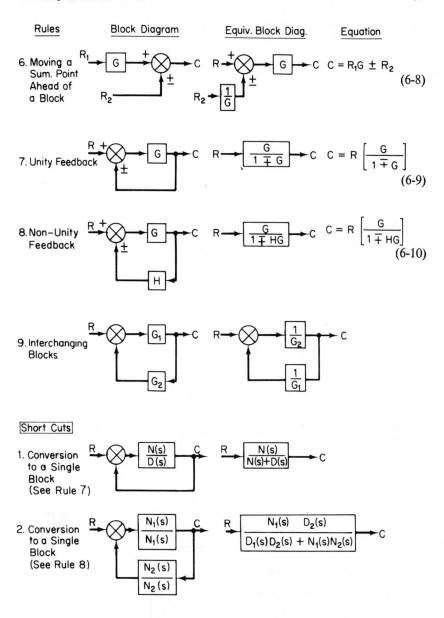

$$C = R_1 G \pm R_2 \qquad (6\text{-}8)$$

6. Moving a Sum. Point Ahead of a Block

7. Unity Feedback

$$C = R \left[\dfrac{G}{1 \mp G} \right] \qquad (6\text{-}9)$$

8. Non–Unity Feedback

$$C = R \left[\dfrac{G}{1 \mp HG} \right] \qquad (6\text{-}10)$$

9. Interchanging Blocks

Short Cuts

1. Conversion to a Single Block (See Rule 7)

2. Conversion to a Single Block (See Rule 8)

3. The Input/Output Ratio Consists of Terms Equal to the Number of Possible Paths from Output to Input, Going <u>Against</u> the Arrows Along the Forward Path and <u>With</u> the Arrows Along the Feedback Path. Each Term is Equal to the Product of All the Feedback Functions Along One Such Path Divided by the Product of All the Forward Functions.

FIG. 6-4. *(Continued)*

Note: Number of Paths = Number of Terms

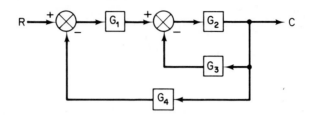

$$\frac{R}{C} = G_4 + \frac{G_3}{G_1} + \frac{1}{G_1 G_2} = \frac{G_1 G_2 G_4 + G_2 G_3 + 1}{G_1 G_2} \quad \& \quad \frac{C}{R} = \frac{G_1 G_2}{G_1 G_2 G_4 + G_2 G_3 + 1}$$

Block Manipulations are Permissible Which do Not Alter
(1) The Product of The G's Between Input and Output or (2) The
Product Around a Feedback Loop.

Block Diagrams For Networks

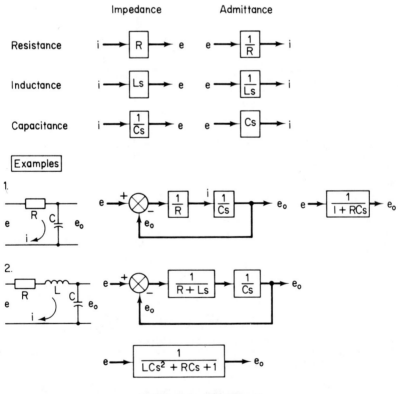

FIG. 6-4. *(Continued)*

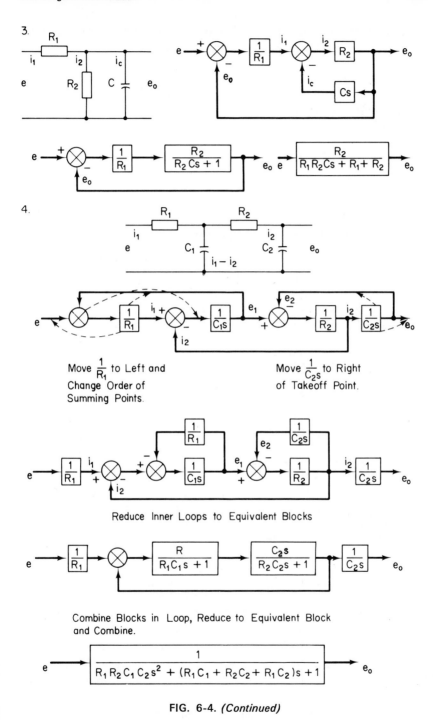

FIG. 6-4. *(Continued)*

Some example problems will now illustrate the theory presented. Figure 6-5 shows the reduction of a block diagram.

EXAMPLE 6-1

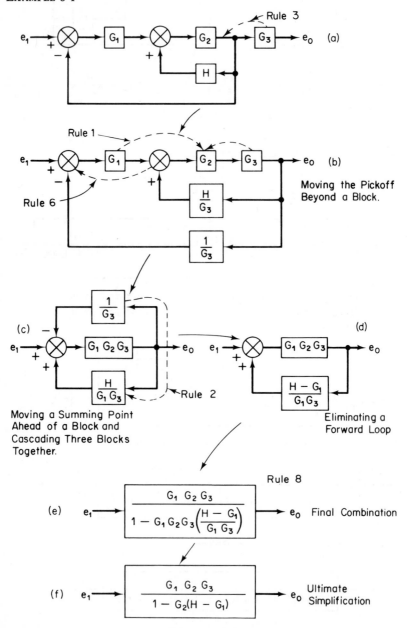

FIG. 6-5. Reduction of a Block Diagram

EXAMPLE 6-2

Given the network shown in figure 6-6. Find the ratio C/R by two methods.

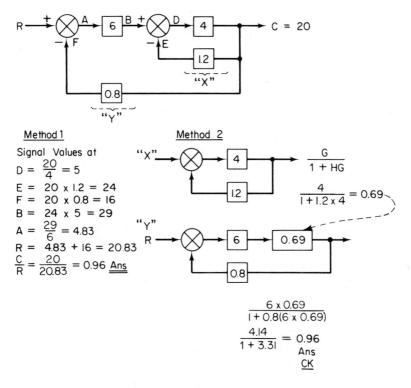

Method 1

Signal Values at

$D = \dfrac{20}{4} = 5$

$E = 20 \times 1.2 = 24$

$F = 20 \times 0.8 = 16$

$B = 24 \times 5 = 29$

$A = \dfrac{29}{6} = 4.83$

$R = 4.83 + 16 = 20.83$

$\dfrac{C}{R} = \dfrac{20}{20.83} = 0.96$ Ans

Method 2

$\dfrac{G}{1 + HG}$

$\dfrac{4}{1 + 1.2 \times 4} = 0.69$

$\dfrac{6 \times 0.69}{1 + 0.8(6 \times 0.69)}$

$\dfrac{4.14}{1 + 3.31} = 0.96$
Ans
CK

FIG. 6-6. Determining Output/Input Ratio

EXAMPLE 6-3

Given the network shown in figure 6-7, find the open-loop gain.

PROBLEMS

1. The following diagram illustrates a voltage divider network:

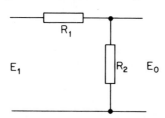

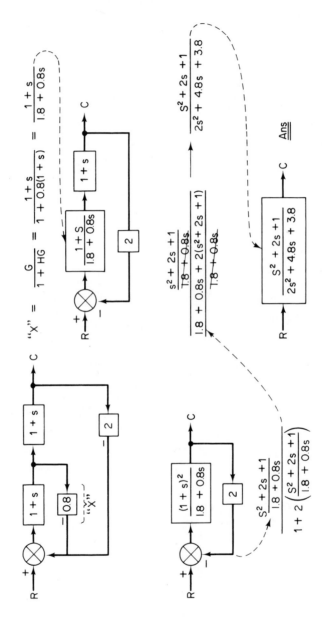

FIG. 6-7. Determining Open-loop Gain

92

(a) Write an equation for E_0 that will give an open-loop system, *i.e.*, as a function of E_1, R_1 and R_2.

(b) Draw the block diagram for problem 1a.

2. Use the voltage divider network of problem 1.

   (a) Write the equation for E_0 in closed-loop form, *i.e.*, as a function of E_1, E_0, R_1 and R_2.

   (b) Draw the block diagram for problem 2a.

   (c) Write the closed-loop transfer function equation.

3. Simplify and determine the open-loop transfer function for the following system.

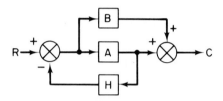

4. Determine the values of R and C of the following system by two methods.

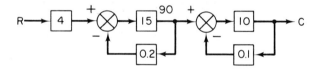

5. Find the transfer function for the following system.

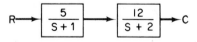

6. Find the transfer function for the following system.

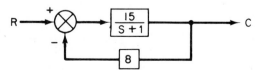

7. Reduce the following network to one overall block diagram.

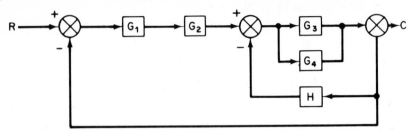

8. Determine the ratio C/R for each of the following systems.

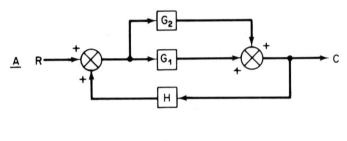

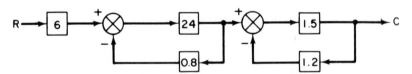

9. Determine the ratio C/R of the following system by two methods.

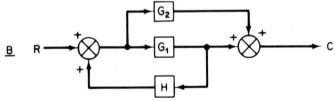

10. Determine the ratio of C/R of the following system.

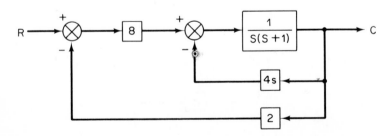

11. Determine the ratio of C/R of the following system.

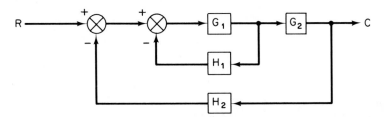

SEVEN

Mechanical electrical characteristics

7.1. GENERAL

In most servo systems, a drive motor is used with other devices such as a gear train, a damper, or a tachometer-generator to position or to rotate a load. The drive motor can be an air motor, a hydraulic motor, or an electric motor. This discussion will concentrate on the electric motor only.

In order to analyze and to determine overall system performance, some mechanical characteristics will be specified, and then the electrical quantities which are analogous will be identified.

7.2. ROTARY MECHANICAL MOTION

FORCES ON A BODY. A body which is set in motion by a force has a number of forces opposing it, *i.e.*, the force is relative to the mass and acceleration and the constants of friction and velocity. This force is equal to

$$f = Ma + Fv \qquad (7\text{-}1)$$

MOMENT OF INERTIA. *Inertia* is the property of a body which resists a change in its velocity in proportion to its mass. *Moment of inertia* refers to the mass of a body in relation to its center of rotation when it is undergoing a change in velocity. It is equal to

$$J = Mr^2 \qquad (7\text{-}2)$$

It may be expressed in gram-centimeter squared, ounce-inch second squared or dyne-centimeter squared.

FRICTION. *Friction* is generally defined as that resistance to motion which occurs when one body is moved in respect to another. In servo systems, the general term friction can be broken down into the following:

1. *Static friction* is the friction that exists when the relative motion is zero. It is often called *stiction*. In a conventional electric-motor drive system, it would be referred to as the starting friction that the motor must overcome in order to set the load in motion.
2. *Coulomb friction* is sometimes called *kinetic friction*, and it is constant and completely independent of relative motion. In terms of surfaces, it would be the friction existing between perfectly dry and smooth surfaces.
3. *Viscous friction* is friction which is proportional to relative motion or velocity and can be likened to the movement of a body through a medium such as gas or liquid. This is the friction specified in the friction constant in equation 7-1. It may be expressed in dyne-centimeter per radian per second, or ounce-inch per radian per second.

ANGULAR POSITION. *Angular position* or *angular displacement* is generally defined as the angle through which a shaft is turned as it moves to a new position, and it is measured in degrees or radians.

ANGULAR VELOCITY. *Angular velocity* is generally defined as a change in angular position per unit of time, *i.e.*, the first derivative of position in respect to time. It may be expressed in revolutions per minute, degrees per second or radians per second, and it is given by

$$\frac{d\theta}{dt} = \frac{\theta}{t} \quad \text{or} \quad \dot{\theta} = \frac{\theta}{t} \tag{7-3}$$

ANGULAR ACCELERATION. *Angular acceleration* is generally defined as a change in angular velocity per unit of time, *i.e.*, the second derivative of position in respect to time. It may be expressed in radians per second squared, and it is given by

$$\frac{d^2\theta}{dt^2} = \frac{\theta}{t^2} \quad \text{or} \quad \ddot{\theta} = \frac{\theta}{t^2} \tag{7-4}$$

TORQUE.   *Torque* is generally defined as the application of a force through a radius, *i.e.*, a distance measured from the center of rotation. It may be expressed in Newton-meter, pound-foot, ounce-inch, dyne-centimeter, etc., and it is given by

$$T = fr \qquad\qquad (7\text{-}5)$$

When defined in terms of moment of inertia and angular acceleration, *inertial torque* is given by

$$T_j = J\ddot{\theta} = J\frac{d^2\theta}{dt^2} \qquad\qquad (7\text{-}6)$$

When defined in terms of viscous friction and angular velocity, *friction torque* is given by

$$T_f = F\dot{\theta} = F\frac{d\theta}{dt} \qquad\qquad (7\text{-}7)$$

POWER.   *Power* is generally defined as the time rate of doing work or a force acting through a distance per unit of time. It may be expressed in horsepower or in watts, depending on size of the drive motor. It is given by

$$P = \frac{W}{t} = \frac{fd}{t} \quad \text{but} \quad f = \frac{T}{r} \quad \text{and} \quad d = r\theta$$

Therefore

$$P = \frac{T}{r}\frac{r\theta}{t}$$

However,

$$r\theta = \frac{d\theta}{dt} \quad \text{so} \quad P = T\frac{d\theta}{dt} = T\dot{\theta}$$

In the "English System,"

$$P = \frac{2\pi \times \text{rpm} \times 746}{33{,}000} \times \frac{T}{16 \times 12} \qquad\qquad (7\text{-}8)$$

which reduces to $P = TS/1352$ with P in watts, T in ounce-inch, and S in rpm.

In the "Metric System,"

$$P = \frac{T \times 141.6}{1352} \times S\frac{2\pi}{60} \qquad\qquad (7\text{-}9)$$

which reduces to $P = Tv$ with P in watts, T in Newton-meters, and v in radians per second.

If the servo uses less than 100W, then it is generally classified as an instrument servo, while if it uses over 100W, the classification falls in the power range.

7.3. GEAR TRAINS

In most servo systems, a gear train is used to connect the servo motor to its load and to transducers used for feedback. A gear train usually accomplishes the following things:

1. It reduces the high speed of a servo motor to the required load speed.
2. It changes the torque of the motor to the required load torque.
3. It may change the direction of rotation of the output shaft in respect to the motor shaft.

A well designed gear train should introduce a minimum of inertia and friction into the system, and, in this respect, it acts the same as an electrical transformer of very high efficiency. The preciseness with which the gears are made and the ratio selected to satisfy the system requirements should provide for optimum performance. The symbol for a gear train in a servo block diagram appears in figure 7-1.

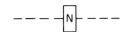

FIG. 7-1. Block Diagram Symbol for a
Gear Train

N is the overall gear ratio of all meshes ($N_1 \times N_2 \times N_3$, etc.) where a mesh consists of two gears such that $N_x = N_L/N_M$, where N_M equals the number of teeth on the motor (drive) gear and N_L equals the number of teeth on the load (driven) gear.

Figure 7-2 shows a motor driving a load through a gear train with associated parameters. These parameters are related in the following manner:

T_M — torque on motor shaft
T_L — torque on load shaft
ω_M — angular velocity of motor
ω_L — angular velocity of load
N_M — number of teeth on motor gear

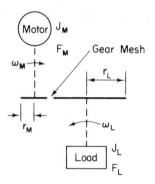

FIG. 7-2. A Simple Gear Mesh

N_L — number of teeth on load gear
N — gear or speed ratio, motor to load
F_M — viscous friction of motor
F_L — viscous friction of load
J_M — actual motor inertia
J_L — actual load inertia
r_M — radius of gear on motor
r_L — radius of gear on load
F — force transmitted between gears
v — velocity of gears

The linear velocity of both gears will be the same, and the forces at the point of contact will be equal and opposite. Therefore

$$v = r_M\omega_M = r_L\omega_L \quad \text{and} \quad \frac{r_M}{r_L} = \frac{\omega_L}{\omega_M} = \frac{1}{N}$$

$$\omega_L = \frac{r_M}{r_L}\,\omega_M = \frac{\omega_M}{N}$$

$$F = \frac{T_M}{r_M} = \frac{T_L}{r_L} \tag{7-10}$$

$$T_L = \frac{r_L}{r_M}\,T_M = NT_M \tag{7-11}$$

$$T_M\omega_M = \frac{T_L}{N}\,(N\omega_L) = T_L\omega_L \tag{7-12}$$

P, the horsepower transmitted by the gear train, is equal to

$$HP = \frac{T_L \omega_L}{550} = \frac{T_M \omega_M}{550} \tag{7-13}$$

while the torque required to accelerate the load inertia alone is

$$T_L = J_L \frac{d\omega_L}{dt} = J_L \alpha_L \tag{7-14}$$

where $d\omega/dt = \alpha =$ angular acceleration in rad/s². Therefore, the power required by the load at the motor shaft is equal to

$$P = \frac{1}{550} \left(J_L \frac{d\omega_L}{dt} \right)$$

$$\omega_L = \frac{1}{550} J_L \frac{d(\omega_M/N)}{dt} \frac{\omega_M}{N}$$

$$= \frac{1}{550} J_L \left(\frac{1}{N} \right)^2 \omega_M \frac{d\omega_M}{dt}$$

$$= \frac{1}{550} J_{LM} \omega_M \frac{d\omega_M}{dt} \tag{7-15}$$

where $J_{LM} = J_L(1/N)^2$ and it is the equivalent inertia load referred to the motor shaft.

This illustrates that the torque required at the motor to accelerate the load can be determined by considering the load to be of an equivalent inertia, J_{LM}, and to be mounted directly on the motor shaft. Thus, total inertia referred to the motor, J_{TM}, that the motor is required to accelerate is equal to

$$J_{TM} = J_M + J_{LM} = J_M + \frac{J_L}{N^2} \tag{7-16}$$

Conversely, if motor inertia is referred to the load shaft, the total inertia of the load and motor referred to the load J_{TL}, is equal to

$$J_{TL} = J_L + J_{ML} = J_L + N^2 J_M \tag{7-17}$$

Thus, load, motor torque, speed, and inertia may be referred from one shaft to the other of a gear train by some function of the gear ratio as follows:

$$T_L = NT_M; \qquad \omega_L = \frac{\omega_M}{N}; \qquad J_{LM} = \frac{J_L}{N^2}; \quad \text{and } J_{ML} = N^2 J_M \quad (7\text{-}18)$$

Any other torques that may be proportional to velocity or position of the motor and load must also have their system constants referred across the gear ratio by the N^2 or $1/N^2$ factor, thus

$$F_{ML} = N^2 F_M \quad \text{and} \quad F_{LM} = \frac{F_L}{N^2} \qquad (7\text{-}19)$$

where F_{ML} is the viscous friction of the motor referred to the load and F_{LM} is the viscous friction of the load referred to the motor. Furthermore,

$$F_{TM} = F_M + F_{LM} = F_M + \frac{F_L}{N^2} \qquad (7\text{-}20)$$

Gearing inefficiency results in the reduction of the torque transmitted through the gear train from the drive gear to the driven gear below that value that would normally appear. Thus, when acceleration requirements of the load are calculated, the load torque and, therefore, the equivalent load inertia must be greater by a factor of $1/u$, where u is the decimal gear efficiency.

TABLE 7-1

Symbol	Parameter	SI	English and/or CGS
J	moment of inertia	kilogram-meter^2	oz-in-s^2
			gm-cm^2
			dyne-cm^2
F	viscous friction		oz-in/rad/s
			dyne-cm/rad/s
T	torque	Newton-meter	lb-ft
			oz-in
			dyne-cm
P	power	watt	watts
			ergs/s
a	angular acceleration	radian/second^2	rad/s^2
			deg/s^2
v	angular velocity	radian/second	rev/min
			rad/s
			deg/s
θ	position (displacement)	radian	radian
			degree

7.4. UNITS AND CONVERSION FACTORS

In many small instrument servos, torque is often expressed in units of ounce-inch, while moment of inertia is given in units of gram-centimeter squared. Thus, it is necessary to be able to go from one set of dimensions to another. This is easily done if conversion factors between systems are understood and used properly.

Table 7-1 shows a number of the most useful parameters in both the SI and English and/or CGS units, while table 7-2 shows some of the most useful conversion factors. For a more complete table of metric and other units, see Appendix A.

TABLE 7-2

Conversion Factors for Servo Calculations

Multiply	By	To Obtain	Multiply	By	To Obtain
Length			*Power*		
meters	39.37	in	(oz-in)(rpm)	7.395×10^{-4}	watts
meters	3.2808	ft	(oz-in)(deg/sec)	1.232×10^{-4}	watts
inches	2.54	cm	(oz-in)(rpm)	9.917×10^{-7}	hp (English)
feet	30.48	cm	(oz-in)(deg/sec)	1.653×10^{-7}	hp (English)
			hp (metric)	1.0138	hp (English)
Mass			*Angular Velocity*		
oz	28.35	gm	rpm	0.1047	rad/s
lb	453.6	gm	rpm	6	deg/s
slug	1.459×10^{-4}	gm	rps	6.2832	rad/s
oz	514.7	slug	deg/s	1.745×10^{-2}	rad/s
lb	3.108×10^{-2}	slug			
Moment of Inertia			*Torque Gradient*		
oz-in^2	182.9	gm-cm^2	oz-in/deg	0.2984	lb-ft/rad
lb-ft^2	4.214×10^5	gm-cm^2	oz-in/deg	4.046×10^6	dyne-cm/rad
slug-ft^2	1.356×10^7	gm-cm^2			
oz-in^2	1.349×10^{-5}	slug-ft^2	*Torque-Inertia Ratio*		
lb-ft^2	3.108×10^{-2}	slug-ft^2	oz-in/gm-cm^2	7.062×10^4	rad/s^2
kg-m^2	141.612	oz-in-sec^2	oz-in/oz-in^2	386.1	rad/s^2
Force					
N (newton)	3.5969	oz			
N (newton)	0.2248	lb			
gm	980.7	dyne			
oz	2.78×10^4	dyne			
lb	4.448×10^5	dyne			
Torque					
Nm	0.7375	lb-ft	(Unless otherwise specified, the		
Nm	141.612	oz-in	units "oz," "lb," and "gm" are		
Nm	10.197×10^4	gm-cm	in units of force.)		
gm-cm	980.7	dyne-cm			
oz-in	7.062×10^4	dyne-cm			
lb-ft	1.356×10^7	dyne-cm			
oz-in	72.01	gm-cm			
lb-ft	7.233×10^{-5}	gm-cm			

7.5. SERVO CHARACTERISTICS

When discussing the characteristics of a servo system, the accuracy and sensitivity of the elements used to represent the command and the controlled output must be considered, both for the static condition and for the dynamic condition. The accuracy with which the elements that are used as error detectors or error correctors are built determines the amount of error that will result when an instrument servo is assembled. Linearity and/or conformity express the accuracy of a precision potentiometer or an LVDT. Resolver or synchro accuracy is given in terms of seconds or minutes of angles. A tachometer-generator, either ac or dc, would have its accuracy given in terms of linearity in respect to volts per revolution.

Sensitivity refers to how well a servo can satisfy the fundamental equation that $e_1 = e_f$ at null. Regardless of whether the servo is an on-off or a bang-bang type, a proportional type or a rate type, the difference between the command, θ_i, and the output, θ_0, must increase to some value before any change is initiated. This value gives the sensitivity of the servo and can be thought of as a *dead band, dead space* or *dead time*. Resolution of the transducers used as error detectors has to be considered when determining the dead band. Electrical noise, lost motion in gear trains or drives, and velocity and acceleration lag, all must be considered. The minimum voltage, either positive or negative, over which a servo motor will respond can also be thought of as dead band.

The sensitivity depends, basically, on the torque gradient or torque constant, K_T, of the servo, and the magnitudes of the torques that the motor must overcome before it starts to rotate. The torque constant is the output torque per unit error angle, and it is equal to

$$T = K_T\theta = K_T V_c \quad \text{or} \quad K_T = \frac{T}{\theta} = \frac{T}{V_c} \tag{7-21}$$

Let us consider a simple position servo of the proportional type. In this servo, the driving torque is proportional to the difference between the command and the controlled output. This output is normally made up of two torques, one required to overcome the viscous friction of the load and the other required to overcome the inertia of the load. The friction load torque is proportional to the control shaft velocity, while the inertia load torque is proportional to the control shaft acceleration. Equation 7-22 gives the relation between these torques and the error.

$$K_T\theta_1 = J\ddot{\theta}_0 + F\dot{\theta}_0 + K_T\theta_0$$
$$K_T\theta_1 - K_T\theta_0 = J\ddot{\theta}_0 + F\dot{\theta}_0 \tag{7-22}$$
$$K_T(\theta_1 - \theta_0) = J\ddot{\theta}_0 + F\dot{\theta}_0$$

If the load were made up of viscous friction only, then the error would be converted directly into output velocity or speed. At zero error, all velocity or motion stops, and the system is at rest. There is no stability problem, but the response time is slow. If the load were made up of inertia only, then continuous oscillation would result. This comes about because, as the error is reduced to zero, acceleration becomes zero but torque still moves the load at a constant speed. As the load overshoots, torque is developed in the opposite direction which decelerates the motor through the zero velocity point and, then reversing the movement, it tries to find the zero error point. This process continues with sustained oscillation.

7.6. ELECTRICAL CIRCUIT ANALOGY

A mechanical servo system which is composed of inertia and friction has an electrical circuit which is analogous to it, *i.e.*, the same mathematical equations will describe their operation. The electric circuit shown in figure 7-3 is a simple R-L-C series connection.

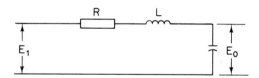

FIG. 7-3. Electrical Analogy of a Mechanical Servo

In this circuit, voltage is the command which determines the charge of the capacitor, and it is thus analogous to torque, which determines the movement of a shaft. In the electric circuit, the current flow and the rate of charge, Q, is determined by the resistance, R. In a mechanical servo, the speed at which the shaft rotates is opposed by the friction constant, F. In the electric circuit, the increase or decrease of current is opposed by inductance, L, while, in the servo, the acceleration of the shaft is opposed by the moment of inertia, J. The error in the mechanical servo is θ which is the difference between the input angle and output angle, while, in the circuit, the error is the difference in charge between that which the input voltage and the output voltage will move through the circuit. In the mechanical servo, the torque constant is K_T, while, in the electric circuit, the corresponding quantity is $1/C$.

Analogous quantities can be tabulated, as in Table 7-3.

TABLE 7-3

Servo Quantity	Electric Quantity
θ_1	$CE_1 = Q_1$
θ_0	$CE_0 = Q_0$
$\theta = \theta_1 - \theta_0$	$Q = Q_1 - Q_0$
$T = K_T \theta$	$E = \dfrac{Q}{C}$
F	R
J	L

The reason for this determination of analogous quantities is that the behavior of the electric circuit can now be analyzed through testing, and the performance of a servo can thus be predicted. For example, damping of a servo may be achieved by mechanical means such as a flywheel or by a resistor-capacitor network with the same end results.

7.7. TEST COMMANDS AND SERVO RESPONSES

GENERAL.   When testing a servo, both static and dynamic characteristics must be considered in regard to accuracy, sensitivity, stability, response, etc. Ideally, perfect accuracy would always be achieved with a resulting infinite sensitivity, but, in practice, there is always some static error, *i.e.*, 117V ± 0.5V or $360° \pm 0.1°$. Accuracy would be

$$\frac{0.5}{117} \times 100 = 0.428\% \quad \text{or} \quad \frac{0.1}{360} \times 100 = 0.028\%$$

Dynamic characteristics are more important in the study and control of servo systems than are static characteristics. The term dynamic means a type of command that is applied to a servo in an everchanging form. Therefore, in the testing and evaluating of a servo, some basic commands are utilized.   These are the step-position, the step-velocity and the sinusoidal command.

STEP-POSITION COMMAND.   This is a situation where the command changes very abruptly from one fixed value to another (either higher or lower). Figure 7-4 shows that the initial value of the command, θ, is zero and, after the unit step change, it rises to a new fixed value.

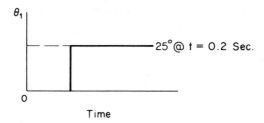

FIG. 7-4. Step Position Command

STEP-VELOCITY COMMAND. This is a situation where the rate of the command changes quite rapidly from one value to another. Figure 7-5 shows that the initial value of the command, θ, is zero, and, after the command, it has a different value. This is often called a *ramp function*.

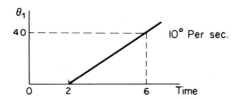

FIG. 7-5. Step Velocity Command

SINUSOIDAL COMMAND. The magnitude of the command varies as a sinusoidal function of time. Figure 7-6 shows such a command with the value of the sinusoid being in the range of 0.1 to 20 hertz.

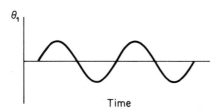

FIG. 7-6. Sinusoidal Command

7.8.   RESPONSE OF A SERVO

The study of the response of a servo to these different commands can be quite complicated because the form of the command may not be a separate one but rather a combination. To simplify the evaluation process, the response can be divided into two different cases, and then each of these cases can be considered separately. These cases are:

1. The *steady state* case where the form of the command is constant so that any effects from any previous change in form have died out. A sinusoidal waveform that is fixed in amplitude and frequency would be considered constant.

2. The *transient* case where the form of the command is changing so that the response of the system is still feeling the effects of the change.

Evaluation of a servo is further broken down into the *time domain region* or the *frequency domain region.*

1. The *time domain region* where the system response is plotted on a graph as the dependent variable with time as the independent variable or as a trace on an oscilloscope.

2. The *frequency domain region* where the system response is plotted on a graph (semilog paper) with its amplitude (20db log) and phase lag or lead as the dependent variable with frequency in hertz or radians/sec as the independent variable.

Figure 7-7 shows how the various commands are used to study the responses for these cases and regions.

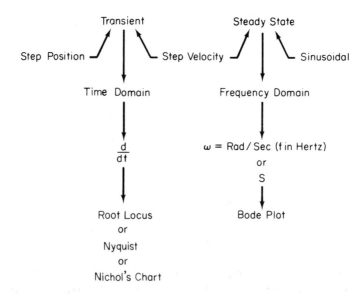

FIG. 7-7. Correlation of Test Commands for Transient and Steady State Test Signals

SOME EXAMPLE PROBLEMS

EXAMPLE 7-1
A servo motor has the following data: $2\emptyset$; 115V; 20W; $T_s = 8$ oz-in; $S_0 = 6000$ rpm; $S_{FL} = 4500$ rpm; $J_m = 0.25$ oz-in-s^2; $J_1 = 24$ gm-cm^2. Determine the following: (1) angular velocity in rad/s at full load, (2) torque developed at full load, (3) acceleration of load in rad/s^2 and (4) speed in rpm for part 3.

(1) $\text{Vel}_{Ang} = \dfrac{S_{FL} \times 2\pi}{60} = \dfrac{4500 \times 6.28}{60} = 471$ rad/s ANS

(2) $T = \dfrac{P \times 1000}{0.746 \times S_{FL}} = \dfrac{20 \times 1000}{0.746 \times 4500} = 6.0$ oz-in ANS

(3) J_L in oz-in-s$^2 = 24$ gm-cm$^2 \times \dfrac{1 \text{ oz-in-s}^2}{7.06 \times 10^4 \text{ gm-cm}^2}$

$= 3.39 \times 10^{-4}$ oz-in-s^2

$\ddot{\theta} = \dfrac{T}{J} = \dfrac{6.0 \text{ oz-in}}{3.39 \times 10^{-4} \text{ oz-in-s}^2} = 17,700$ rad/s^2 ANS

(4) $5 = \sqrt{\dfrac{\ddot{\theta}}{2\pi}} \times 60 = \sqrt{\dfrac{17,700 \text{ rad/s}^2}{6.28}} \times 60 = 3185$ rpm ANS

EXAMPLE 7-2
An inertia load of $J = 10.6$ gm-cm^2 is subjected to a torque of 3.5 oz-in. What acceleration in rad/s^2 is imparted to the load?

$$\ddot{\theta} = \frac{T}{J} = \frac{3.5 \text{ oz-in}}{10.6 \text{ gm-cm}^2 \left(\dfrac{1 \text{ oz-in-s}^2}{7.06 \times 10^4 \text{ gm-cm}^2} \right)}$$

$$= 23,300 \text{ rad/s}^2 \text{ ANS}$$

EXAMPLE 7-3
A servo motor is rated at 4W. If it is delivering 2.4 oz-in of torque to its load, at what speed is it running?

$$P = \frac{ST}{1352} \quad \text{and} \quad S = \frac{P \times 1352}{T}$$

$$S = \frac{4 \times 1352}{2.4} = 2250 \text{ rpm ANS}$$

EXAMPLE 7-4

A step position command of 12° and a step velocity command of 16 deg/s are both introduced at time t = 0. At what time will the step velocity command be twice the step-position command?

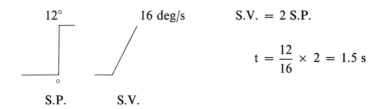

12°   16 deg/s   S.V. = 2 S.P.

$$t = \frac{12}{16} \times 2 = 1.5 \text{ s}$$

S.P.   S.V.

PROBLEMS

1. A shaft is rotating at 3600 rpm. What is its angular velocity in rad/s?

2. A shaft is rotating at an angular velocity of 293 rad/s. What is its speed in rpm?

3. What is the angular velocity in deg/s for a motor that is rotating at 2400 rpm?

4. A motor is rotating at an angular velocity of 12 deg/s. What is its speed in rpm?

5. A motor is rotating at 32 rad/s, and the power input is 24W. What is the driving torque at the shaft?

6. A step-position command of 15° and a step-velocity command of 18 deg/s are both introduced at time t = 0. At what time will they be equal to each other?

7. A step-position command and a step-velocity command are both equal at time t = 2.4 s. If the step-position command is 9.8°, what is the step-velocity command in deg/s?

8. A servo motor develops a torque of 0.12 oz-in at 3200 rpm. What is the power developed?

9. A load has an inertia, J, of 21.2 gm-cm². The torque delivered to this load by the motor is 7.2 oz-in. Find the acceleration of the load in rad/s².

10. For the motor and load of problem 9, find the speed in rpm.

11. A servo system has the ability to position a pointer with an accuracy of 24 minutes out of 360°. The 360° represent one mile in distance. What is the accuracy in percent?

12. A proportional zero has a moment of inertia of 2.36 gm-cm^2. What is the moment of inertia in oz-in-s^2?

13. A 4W servo motor has a load speed of 4800 rpm. What is the torque in oz-in?

14. A potentiometer of 10K ohms is connected across 48V. It can rotate through an angle of 353°. What is the voltage gradient? What percent accuracy will allow a deviation of 0.065 volts/degree?

EIGHT

Analysis of servomotors and generators

8.1. GENERAL

In early servomechanisms, both ac and dc servomotors had been used; with the ac predominating, mainly because an ac squirrel-cage induction motor is rugged, easy to use, and performs well. Even though the dc motor was more efficient, it was less reliable because of brush problems and radio frequency interference. DC motors were used mainly for high power servomechanisms, while the ac motor dominated the instrument servo field.

However, the introduction of new magnetic material has brought forth radically new and superior motor configurations which has led to increased performance advantages of the dc motor. The brush problem has been resolved so that increased reliability and reduced RF1 have been achieved. AC amplifiers are inherently more stable than dc amplifiers, but they are also more expensive. AC line power is more readily available than dc power, but most amplifiers require a dc supply. DC signals and dc feedback are more practical because phasing problems are eliminated and compensation is simplified.

8.2. APPLICATION FACTORS

Servomechanisms which generate less than 100W are considered instrument servos, and, in this power range, the two-phase ac servomotor has been the major selection especially when signals, power input and excitation levels come from a carrier frequency of either 60Hz or 400Hz. Low level dc signals, coming from thermocouples, strain gages, etc., are fed through a modulator, which converts the dc to ac, are amplified, and are then used to drive an ac motor.

DC servomotors should be used where the required output demands fast response and high efficiency; also, a dc system is simpler and lower in cost. The systems are simpler and smaller because present-day, operational amplifiers practically eliminate the drift that was characteristic of older dc amplifiers. Heat sinking and cooling method advances as well as pulse width modulation techniques are also factors. DC motors can deliver peak power well above the steady power rating; for these reasons, a smaller motor is used. As an example, chart recorders which require a wide bandwidth almost invariably use dc motors. Large inertial loads are another example. In general, where applications are for moderately accurate, short life (less than 1000 full-speed operating hours), non-militarized systems, dc systems should be used. If the requirements are for high accuracy, long life, rugged and compact systems, then ac systems should be used. An exception to this is the use of dc torque motors which eliminate the need for gear trains.

Electrically, torque is produced in a motor by interaction between armature current and field flux. Maximum torque is obtained when the current and flux are in time phase together. Therefore, in ac motors, space and time-phase deviations result in a lower torque output. In an ac motor, transformer action through the stator magnetic field generates the rotor current and flux. As very small transformers are inefficient, so are small induction motors. In addition the peak flux density is $\pi/2$ times the average flux density; therefore, the iron in the induction motor is increased, by 57% to be exact, which results in inefficiency. DC motors receive their rotor (armature) energy directly by conduction through the brushes. The iron losses are considerably less, and, even though armature reaction is present, it lies along the interpolar axis so that less iron is required in the dc motor. All of these factors lead to higher dc efficiency.

8.3. FUNDAMENTAL EQUATION

The fundamental equation (applicable to both two-phase induction motors and dc servomotors) relates motor torque, speed, and power.

$$T_S = \frac{1352}{S_0} P_R \tag{8-1}$$

where T_S is the stall torque in oz-in, S_0 is the no load (free) speed in rpm, and P_R is the stall power to rotor in watts.

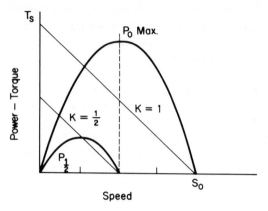

FIG. 8-1. A Comparison of Motor Power Output and
Motor Torque

The motor must be capable of producing more power than the load requires. The speed of the motor when it is driving the load at rated voltage should be above one-half the free speed. This allows the motor to operate on the negative slope of the power curve. Thus, as the load increases, the operating point moves toward the point of maximum power. As the maximum speed decreases, the theoretical torque per watt increases. The inherent damping—which equals T_S/S_0, slope of the lines—increases rapidly as the free speed decreases (see figure 8-1). As the motor speed is reduced in respect to the load, less gearing is required which is why dc torque motors usually serve as direct drive in closed-loop servos.

AC servomotors have numerous poles with a lower synchronous speed which increases internal damping. However, the efficiency of power transfer to the rotor decreases rapidly as the number of poles increases. Thus, ac motors have a limit to the number of poles; dc motors do not have this limit because dc free speed decreases as magnetic field strength increases. The newer magnetic materials allow free speed to be reduced to a level well below the value for comparable ac motors.

Torque efficiency in dc motors is almost 100%; this means that nearly all the input stall power is converted to torque. In an ac motor, it is a very complex function. Brush friction and voltage drop are the principal loss factors in small dc motors. The basic torque equation shows that developed torque per watt in a dc motor depends only on the free speed which is inversely proportional to magnetic field strength. In ac motors, the magnetic field strength comes from the transformer action of magnetizing current. For efficient operation, this means very small air gaps are needed.

8.4. AC SERVOMOTORS

The conventional ac servo motor is a two-phase induction motor which usually contains a squirrel-cage rotor and operates on the same principles as a transformer with the stator acting as the primary winding and the rotor acting as the secondary winding. Usually, a fixed voltage is applied to the reference phase, and a variable voltage is applied to the control phase. These voltages create a rotating magnetic field in the stator which, by transformer action, induces currents in the rotor; the rotor will then revolve in the direction of the rotating magnetic field. The torque required by the load determines the rotor speed.

If a two-phase power supply is not available, then the motor can be connected across a single-phase supply. However, in order to get the 90° effect of a two-phase supply, it is necessary to connect a capacitor either in series or in parallel with the reference winding. The control winding is then connected across the output from a servo amplifier which means that there is a variable voltage across it, and thus there is a variable torque output of the motor.

Figure 8-2 shows the approximate normal characteristics of a two-phase motor having essentially straight speed torque curves. Most of the performance characteristics of the motor can be predicted from these curves. The shape of these curves is governed almost entirely by rotor resistance. With high resistance, a more linear curve results, but the maximum torque is less. The more sloping the curves, the more that damping becomes inherent in the motor. The speed at which the motor operates with rated voltage on both windings and no external load is called the *free speed*. The torque at zero speed is the *stall torque*.

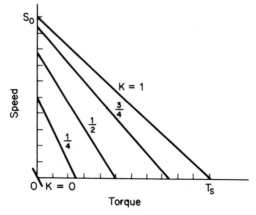

FIG. 8-2. Speed Torque Characteristics for Different Values of Control Voltages

The available torque is given by equation 8-2:

$$T = T_s - \frac{T_s}{S_0} \times \frac{d\theta}{dt} \qquad (8\text{-}2)$$

However, $T_s = K_T V_C$ where K_T is the proportionality constant between stall torque and control field voltage. The torque, T, that is generated to give acceleration at any speed or voltage is

$$T = K_T V_C - \frac{T_s}{S_0} \frac{d\theta}{dt} \qquad (8\text{-}3)$$

and as this torque accelerates the rotor inertia, J:

$$K_T V_C = J \frac{d^2\theta}{dt^2} + \frac{T_s}{S_0} \frac{d\theta}{dt} \qquad (8\text{-}4)$$

This torque consists of two components. One is utilized to accelerate the rotor inertia while the other accelerates the viscous friction constant, T_s/S_0. This constant is the slope of the speed-torque curve, is represented by F, and represents the viscous damping of the motor and is usually expressed in dyne-centimeters per rad per second, or in ounce-inch/radian per second. See figure 8-3.

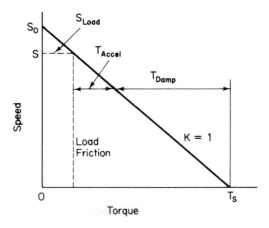

FIG. 8-3. Speed Torque Relationships for a Servomotor

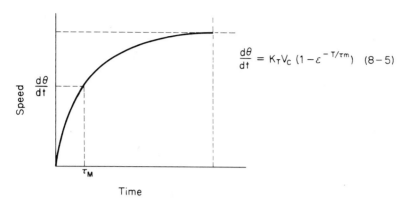

FIG. 8-4. Motor Speed as a Function of Time

As the control field voltage is reduced, the slope of the speed-torque curves (or the damping) decreases. Damping at low control voltages is about one-quarter to one-half the damping at rated voltage. This is an important consideration, especially in a position servomechanism, because the operating point is usually at or near zero control voltage and zero speed. It is at this point that stability is the hardest to achieve because of gearing backlash, transducer resolution and other effects.

If rated voltage is applied to the motor at rest, most of the torque that is developed will be used to accelerate the rotor inertia because the friction constant at the instant of starting is zero. However, as the speed increases, the viscous friction or damping will come into effect more and more, and the acceleration will decrease. The relationship between instantaneous speed, $d\theta/dt$, and time at any instant is an exponential function, as is shown in figure 8-4. J/F is the time constant of the motor.

$$\frac{d\theta}{dt} = K_T V_C (1 - \varepsilon^{-T/\tau_M}) \qquad (8\text{-}5)$$

8.5.   DC SERVOMOTORS

It was mentioned before that the need for high power output and fast response has brought the dc motor back into the servo picture. The different types of dc motors are the wound-field type (shunt, series, and compound wound), the printed-circuit motor, the moving-coil motor, the direct-drive dc torquer, the permanent magnet motor, and the stepper motor. The stepper motor will not be covered in this chapter, but it will be discussed in Chapter 12 mainly because it is a digital device, rather than one of continuous rotation.

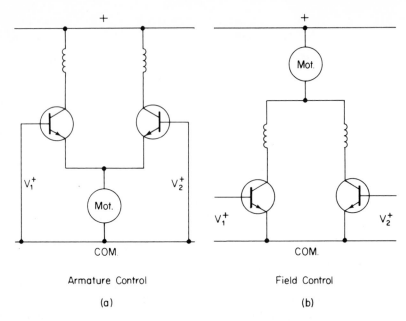

FIG. 8-5. Basic dc Wound-field Motor Connections Using Transistors

WOUND-FIELD TYPE

DC motors can be controlled by varying the current to either the armature or the field. In many motors, the field winding is split into two sections. If both windings have the same current flow, then the two magnetic fields oppose, and no motor action takes place. However, if one of the field voltages is higher than the other, then the motor will run with the direction of rotation being governed by the winding that has the largest voltage and current. The motor is called a *split-series field motor*; its connection is shown in figure 8-5.

In figure 8-5(a), the motor is connected for armature control with the fields acting as the load for the NPN transistors. The polarity and value of the voltage at V1 or V2 will determine the direction of rotation because this governs which field is excited. The counter emf of the motor will appear between the emitter and ground so that V1 or V2 must be increased in order to increase the speed. When V1 is increased, the transistor is momentarily forward biased to a greater degree which increases the collector current and field current. The increase in field current increases the motor current which causes an increase in motor speed. The counter emf will thus increase; this tends to reduce the emitter and collector current, and the speed stabilizes. If V1 is held constant, then as load is increased, the speed will decrease, the armature and field current will rise a little, and so will the torque. This results in a sloping speed-torque characteristic which is desired. In either case, V1 or V2 being used, a certain minimum voltage is required to start the motor rotating in either direction.

In figure 8-5(b), the motor is connected for field control with the armature acting as the load for the NPN transistors. The transistor current is determined by the value of the voltage at V1 or V2. In this connection, if the motor is unloaded, the speed will increase to a very high value for a small change in input voltage. The reason for this is that for this transistor connection, the motor has the no-load high speed characteristic of the series motor; thus, as biasing is increased, the field current rises with a corresponding rise in speed. As load is applied, the motor slows down very rapidly in order to allow the collector current to increase somewhat so that the required torque is produced.

Of the two connections, armature control requires a larger driving signal, but it is much easier to control; field control is quite a bit more sensitive, but it is harder to control in a system in terms of stability.

PERMANENT MAGNET (PM) TYPE

A permanent magnet (PM) motor is one in which a permanent magnet replaces the field windings, thus saving on copper, armature size, and power to energize the field. The PM motor is usually well compensated by commutating windings so that the field magnets are not demagnetized whenever the armature voltage is suddenly reversed or sudden overloads or stalling result. Operating in high temperatures may also cause a decrease in PM flux. The main advantages of a PM motor are that they (1) are smaller and lighter than wound-field motors of the same rating, (2) have a linear speed-torque relationship, (3) have a high starting torque, and (4) only two wires are needed, rather than four.

The magnets for almost all PM motors are made from a form of Alnico VIII alloy cast in a circular ring and completely surrounding the armature. However, a new magnet material composed of samarium (a rare earth element), cobalt, and some additives imparts flux properties that are quite a bit above those of the Alnico series. Unfortunately, this material is extremely expensive, so motors that are made with the samarium magnet are restricted to special applications, mostly military, medical pacemakers, and some computer areas. Their biggest advantages are their low moment of inertia, fast response and high torque.

Another type of PM motor that may eventually come into use as a servo motor is the brushless dc motor that uses the samarium magnets and electronic, rather than mechanical, commutation. The electronic commutation is achieved by using several different techniques such as optical, rf, resolver, and Hall-effect semiconductor devices.

DIRECT-DRIVE TORQUE MOTOR TYPES

The direct-drive torque motor is a permanent magnet type of motor that can rotate continuously after the introduction of an electric signal so as to maintain zero error in a position or speed control system. They are constructed with a frameless type of housing, of large diameter but rather narrow, and they have fairly large axial holes through the rotor for connections to various shafts and bosses. They operate well at low speeds with high torque to inertia ratio and with zero-coupling loss or backlash because of the direct load connection. Commutation at the higher speeds causes sparking and also contributes to sensitivity ripple; ripple is a variation in torque or generated voltage as the brushes switch the conductors. Cogging, which is the change in air gap reluctance as the rotor revolves, is a residual effect that sometimes limits the motor torque performance. Building the rotor with skewed laminations and bridging the poles may help to eliminate cogging. Another way is to use a slotless rotor.

The two methods of controlling power to dc torque motors are pulse width modulation and proportional control. Pulse width modulation uses either SCR's or transistors with high efficiency, but it gives sluggish responses with fairly large ripple torque. Proportional control is usually accomplished via a bridge circuit of transistors with two operating as linear amplifiers and two operating to switch the power supply connections to the motor.

The direct-drive dc torque motor eliminates the gear train used with most servomotors, and, thus, the system must be analyzed somewhat differently because of its large bandwidth and high performance.

MOVING-COIL DC MOTOR TYPES

The moving-coil motor is a permanent magnet type of motor that has either a flat disc armature or a shell armature that contains no iron. The copper armature conductors in the shell style are held in place by non-magnetic materials such as epoxy, polymer resins and fiber glass. The armature of the disc style may be made by photoetching a disc or from preformed segments. The disc type motor is often called the *printed-circuit* motor. The active armature conductors of either style move through an air gap of high flux density but with no reluctance torque effect or cogging.

The moving-coil motor has the highest acceleration capability of any dc motor, *i.e.*, several thousand start-stop duty cycles per second, so it is generally used for incremental motion control rather than for continuous high speed performance. The torque to inertia ratio of a shell type armature may reach 1,000,000 rad/s^2. Because of these desirable characteristics, these motors are used extensively in the data-processing industry, numerical control of machine tools, textile drives and any application requiring high efficiency, high performance, and high acceleration rates.

PRINTED-CIRCUIT MOTOR TYPE

The printed-circuit motor is in reality the disc moving-coil type with a printed-circuit armature/commutator that gives a very compact, low inertia unit. The armature is made of copper with a large number of commutator segments which ensure a smooth, noncogging output mainly because the inductance of the printed armature is so low that it is considered zero for all practical purposes. This is true because the armature has very few turns with poor inductive coupling to the permanent magnet field structure.

The principal advantages of the printed-circuit motor are (1) low time constant, (2) high pulse torque, (3) minimal cogging, (4) wide speed range, and (5) efficient heat transfer. These advantages have allowed the motor to be used successfully in both velocity and positioning servo systems; in incremental motion drives such as punched-card readers/punches, programmable stepping servos, paper feed mechanisms for printers, line-by-line reading and punching of paper tape, disc file magnetic head actuator; and in many other systems. In most of these applications, a low inertia load must be started and stopped rapidly and repeatedly either in fixed increments or in a random but programmable manner. Such a motor is necessary to drive successfully the load at the high repetition rates involved. In some cases, the stepping motion of the servo may have to be inhibited in order to *slew* through large shaft displacements. This is true because any time given up to motion is really a lost time; thus, the slew operation must be completed at the highest speed compatible with the system's capability.

Figure 8-6 shows a block diagram of an incremental servo of Type 0 (see figure 10-7). The motor has a standard dc tachometer, and it is driven from a servo amplifier. In this type system, under normal operation as a regulator, any difference between the input voltage and the tachometer voltage will just be sufficient to drive the servo motor and to maintain the desired load speed.

Incremental motion control is obtained by operating the servo in a nonlinear mode. Explanation for this is given by reference to the waveforms of figure 8-7 and is outlined as follows.

A step command voltage, 1–2, is applied to the input at time t_0. Since the motor cannot respond instantly, a large error signal, 3–4, which exceeds the saturation level of the amplifier is produced; thus, the full amplifier output voltage, 5–6, is applied to the motor. The

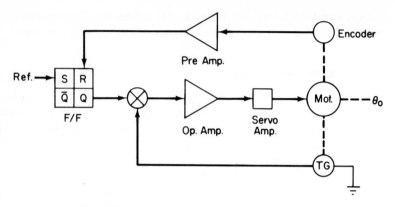

FIG. 8-6. Block Diagram of an Incremental Servo

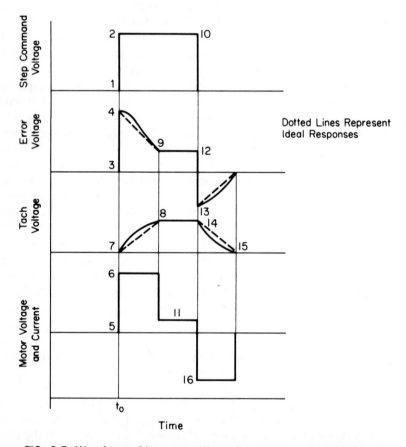

FIG. 8-7. Waveforms of Incremental Servo Response to a Step Command

motor then accelerates, 7–8, and, as this happens, the tachometer voltage increases and reduces the error until the error signal falls within the tolerance band, 9, and the system stabilizes.

If the step voltage drops to zero, at 10, the reverse of the above operation will take place and can be easily traced. The level of voltage and current required to supply the load torque is shown at 11.

8.6.   EVALUATION FACTORS

Other factors to be considered when analyzing motor operation and characteristics are (1) dead band, (2) torque constant, (3) velocity constant, (4) moment of inertia, and (5) the motor transfer function. Let us examine each of these in order.

DEAD BAND

In the strict sense, dead band is defined as the specified range of values over which the incoming signal can be varied without causing the output to respond. In a servo motor, it is the range of applied voltage just before the motor starts to rotate in either direction for a given amplifier gain. For an ac servo motor, this means that there is full voltage on the reference phase and zero volts on the control phase. As the control-phase voltage is slowly increased, a point is reached at which the motor just starts to turn. If the polarity of the voltage is reversed, the same thing will happen, but the motor will start in reverse. For a dc servo motor, it is the applied voltage, either to the field or armature depending on how they are controlled, which will just cause the motor to start. This starting point is also called the *threshold*, and it is clearly shown in figure 8-8. The dead

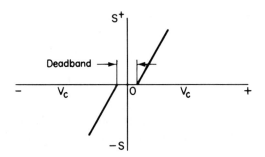

FIG. 8-8. Deadband of a Servomotor

band is due to a number of different things including friction of the gear train and load, inertia of the load and motor rotor, and certain magnetic effects.

If a potentiometer or synchro transducer with a sensitivity in volts per degree is supplying the error signal to the amplifier, then the dead band can be determined by applying equation 8-6 with twice the angle being the dead band.

$$2 \times V_C = D.B.^\circ \times K_S \times K_A$$

$$D.B.^\circ = \frac{2V_C}{K_S K_A} \qquad (8\text{-}6)$$

with K_S being CT sensitivity in volts/degrees, K_A being amplifier gain in volts/volt, and V_C being control voltage in volts.

It is clear from equation 8-6 that the sensitivity of a system can be improved by reducing the dead band, and the easiest way to do this is to increase the gain of the amplifier. However, increasing the gain may lead to instability; therefore, a compromise must be reached. It can also be seen that if an application requires a certain dead band and the transducers and motor have been selected, then the required gain can be calculated so that an amplifier can be specified.

TORQUE CONSTANT—K_T

The torque constant is the torque per armature ampere or the torque per armature volt that the motor can develop with constant field flux. In servo treatment, it is generally considered to be the ratio between the stall torque and control voltage. For an ac servo motor, it means rated voltage on the reference phase with the starting or stall torque being directly proportional to the voltage on the control phase. For a dc servo motor, it is the stall torque developed for the impressed voltage on either the field or armature. For either motor, it is given by

$$K_T = \frac{T_S}{V_C} \qquad (8\text{-}7)$$

with T_S being stall torque and V_C being control voltage.

VELOCITY CONSTANT—K_V

The velocity constant is a proportionality constant between motor speed and control voltage and represents the speed in radians per second that the motor can develop for every one volt that is impressed on it. It is expressed as

$$K_V = \frac{S}{V_C} \qquad (8\text{-}8)$$

with S being speed or velocity and V_C being control voltage. K_V may also be found from the torque constant, K_T, and the viscous damping factor, F, of the motor. The damping factor is equal to T_S/S_0, so:

$$K_V = \frac{K_T}{F_T} \qquad (8\text{-}9)$$

but $K_T = T_S/V_C$ and $F = T_S/S_0$; therefore:

$$K_V = \frac{T_S/V_C}{T_S/S_0} = \frac{S_0}{V_C}$$

with S_0 being in rad/s and V_C being in volts. This constant is important when the steady-state response of a servo is being considered after it is subjected to a step-velocity command because it represents how fast a motor will respond to a one volt error change.

MOMENT OF INERTIA

In many instrument type servos, the load consists only of a dial pointer or data device such as a recorder pen; therefore, the moment of inertia of the motor rotor represents the main retarding force to angular motion. This moment of inertia, as is outlined in section 7-2, is usually expressed in gram-centimeter squared or ounce-inch-second squared.

MOTOR TRANSFER FUNCTION

This is the ratio between the motor output, in terms of angular movement, and the input control voltage; it combines most of the motor terms discussed in sections 7-2 and 8-4. It may be inserted into a system block diagram in the following way:

$$K_T\theta = J\ddot{\theta} + F\dot{\theta}_0 \quad \text{but} \quad K_T\theta \cong K_T V_C \qquad (8\text{-}10)$$

Now convert equation 8-10 to the LaPlace operator

$$K_T V_C = Js^2\theta_0 + Fs\theta_0$$

Factor θ_0 out so

$$K_T V_C = \theta_0(Js^2 + Fs)$$

Rearrange

$$\frac{\theta_0}{V_C} = \frac{K_T}{Js^2 + Fs}$$

Divide by F:

$$\frac{\theta_0}{V_C} = \frac{K_T/F}{(J/F)s^2 + s}$$

But $K_T/F = K_V$ and $J/F = \tau$ (time constant)

$$\therefore \frac{\theta_0}{V_C} = \frac{K_V}{s + \tau s^2} = \frac{K_V}{s(1 + \tau s)} \qquad (8\text{-}11)$$

$$V_C \longrightarrow \boxed{\frac{K_V}{s(1 + \tau s)}} \longrightarrow \theta_0$$

8.7.   SERVO GENERATORS

Many applications in servo systems, especially in the instrument servo range, require a voltage which is proportional to the rate of change of some function such as position or speed. This voltage may be used as a shaft speed readout or as a stabilization voltage in a closed-loop system. Such a device is called a *rate generator* or a *tachometer-generator*.

The ac rate generator usually consists of a two-phase stator, a drag cup, and a rotor of nonmagnetic material. An ac reference voltage is applied to one phase, thus setting up a magnetic field. The second phase is located 90° mechanically from the first. When the drag cup is rotated between the two windings, a second field is produced at approximately right angles to the first. This field produces an output voltage which is a direct function of the rotor shaft velocity. A change in direction of rotation causes a 180° phase shift in the polarity of the output voltage. The positive direction of rotation gives an output voltage that is in-phase with the reference input.   Conversely, an out-of-phase voltage means reverse rotation. Figure 8-9 shows the schematic diagram.

The rate generator is used for three basic applications, *i.e.*, (1) as speed or rate control for a servo, (2) as integrating or angular position servos, and (3) as a stabilizing device for a position servo. When it is used in a speed control system, the output of the rate generator is compared to the command or reference input signal. If the desired output of a speed control system is angular position rather than angular speed, then integration is performed by the rate generator. The third application, which is velocity damping, uses the rate generator to simulate a higher viscous friction. Increasing the viscous friction in respect to the moment of inertia decreases the system time constant, and thus permits higher

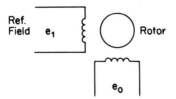

FIG. 8-9. A Two-phase Rate Generator

amplifier gain. Higher gain with the same stability usually means better system operation.

The dc tachometer-generator usually consists of a permanent magnet field with a wound armature. The output voltage of the armature is proportional to the shaft velocity and is quite linear; therefore, over its range of operation, it is free from random input voltage changes in the operating frequency ranges. Also the voltage gradient, *i.e.*, volts per rpm, should be stable with any changes in ambient or device temperature. The polarity of the voltage is determined by the direction of rotation.

The rate generator or tachometer-generator is quite often constructed integrally with the servo motor on the same shaft. This makes mounting easier and, at the same time, still gives high performance characteristics.

Some example problems will now illustrate the theory presented.

EXAMPLE 8-1

Given the following servo motor data: $2\emptyset$ 115V 20W $T_s = 8$ oz-in; $S_0 = 6000$ rpm; $S_{FL} = 4500$ rpm; and $J_M = 6.5 \times 10^{-4}$ oz-in-s^2. Determine the following: (1) slope of characteristic curve, (2) torque constant, K_T, in oz-in/V, (3) velocity constant, K_V, in rad/s/V, (4) time constant, T, and (5) transfer function in frequency response form.

Solution

(1) Slope $F = -\dfrac{T_s}{S_0} = -\dfrac{8 \text{ oz-in}}{6000 \text{ rpm}} \times \dfrac{60}{2\pi} = -0.013$ oz-in/rad/s ANS

(2) $K_T = \dfrac{T_s}{V_C} = \dfrac{8 \text{ oz-in}}{115V} = 0.07$ oz-in/V ANS

(3) $K_V = \dfrac{K_T}{F} = \dfrac{0.07 \text{ oz-in/V}}{0.013 \text{ oz-in/rad/s}} = 5.36$ rad/s/V ANS

(4) $\tau = \dfrac{J}{F} = \dfrac{6.5 \text{ oz-in-s}^2 \times 10^{-4}}{0.013 \text{ oz-in/rad/s}} = 0.05$ s ANS

(5) $\dfrac{\dot{\theta}_0}{V_C} = \dfrac{K_V}{s(1 + \tau s)} = \dfrac{5.36}{s(1 + 0.05s)} = \dfrac{5.36 \times 20}{s(20 + s)} = \dfrac{107}{s^2 + 20s}$ ANS

EXAMPLE 8-2

A two-phase servo motor will start when the applied voltage to its control phase equals 6% of rated voltage. The CT of the synchro pair used as transducers has a sensitivity of 0.64 volts/degree. The rated control voltage is 30V. The amplifier gain equals 36dB. Determine the following: (1) the dead band in degrees, and (2) the gain if the dead band is tripled.

Solution

(1) $2V_s = D.B.^\circ\ K_S K_A$

   $K_A = 36dB$ or 63

   $D.B.^\circ = \dfrac{2 \times 30 \times 0.06V}{63 \times 0.64V/deg} = \dfrac{3.6^\circ}{40.32} = 0.089^\circ$ ANS

(2) $K_A = \dfrac{2 \times 30}{3 \times 0.089 \times 0.64}$

   $= 351$ K_A in dB   (m = 20 Log M)   M = 351   m = 20 × 2.55

   $K_A = 50.9dB$ ANS

EXAMPLE 8-3

A dc permanent magnet servo motor has the following data: 50V 1800 rpm $K_T = 5.25$ oz-in/V; and $R_{ia} = 8$ ohm. Determine the free speed and stalled torque for applied voltages of 50V, 40V, 30V and 20V. Also sketch the curves for the different voltages.

Solution

(1) $K_G = \dfrac{V}{S_0} = \dfrac{50}{1800} = 0.928V/rpm$ $\therefore$

V	S_0	T_s
50	1800	262.5
40	1430	210
30	1070	158
20	715	105

   $T_S = K_T V_C = 5.25$ oz-in/V × 50V

   $= 262.5$ oz-in

   $S_{040} = \dfrac{40}{0.028} \times 1800 = 1430$ rpm

   $T_{S40} = \dfrac{40}{50} \times 262.5 = 210$ oz-in

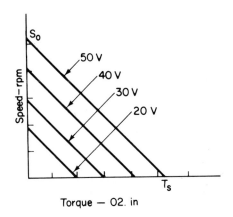

Torque — 02. in

PROBLEMS

1. A dc servo motor has the following data: Permanent magnet 120V 1500 rpm K_T = 105.6 oz-in/armature ampere; and R_{ia} = 6 ohms. Determine the free speed and stalled torque for different applied voltages of 120V, 90V, 70V, 50V and 30V. Also plot the family of curves.

2. A two-phase servo motor will start when the voltage applied to its control phase equals 5% of rated. The sensitivity of the synchro CT is 0.393 volts/degree. The rated control phase voltage is 35V. Calculate the amplifier gain if the desired dead band equals 0.1°.

3. A two-phase servo motor will start when the applied voltage to its control phase equals 5% of rated. The sensitivity of the synchro CT is 1.0 volts/degree. The rated control phase voltage is 26V. The amplifier gain equals 100 or 40dB. Calculate the dead band in degrees.

4. A permanent magnet dc motor has the following parameters:

armature inertia	2.0 oz-in-s^2
T_S at 30V	5 oz-in
S_0 at 30V	4800 rpm

Determine (a) friction constant, F, in oz-in/rad/s, and (b) the time in seconds it takes the motor to reach a speed of 3000 rpm.

5. A servo motor, Kearfott R110-2, has a mechanical time constant of 0.038 seconds and an electrical time constant of 0.0007 seconds. It has a velocity constant of 12 rad/s/volt. Determine the motor transfer function.

6. A two-phase servo motor has the following data:

$$\text{Phase voltages} = 115V; \quad T_s = 5 \text{ oz-in}; \quad S_0 = 4500 \text{ rpm};$$

and

$$J = 0.2 \text{ oz-in-s}^2$$

Determine the motor transfer function.

7. A constant speed application takes a regulating signal from a tachometer-generator sensing device. The regulator requires a signal change of 0.1V to produce the necessary corrections.
   (a) If the allowable error at maximum speed is 1%, what voltage must the tachometer-generator produce at maximum speed?
   (b) What tachometer-generator voltage is required at the maximum speed to reduce the allowable error to 0.5%? 0.25%?
   (c) What conclusion can be made relative to the magnitude of the signal level where a choice exists?

8. A speed-indicating device consists of a two-pole permanent magnet dc tachometer-generator with a dc voltmeter connected to its terminals. The generator has an armature with 1,000 conductors having two parallel paths and a resistance of 1,000 ohms between brushes. The air gap flux is 36,000 lines per pole. The dc voltmeter which is connected directly across the brushes has a resistance of 2,000 ohms. What speed in RPM will be indicated by a reading of 5V on the voltmeter?

9. What is the transfer function of the tachometer-generator of problem 8?

10. A servo motor has a time constant of 0.026 seconds, a free speed of 6500 rpm and a rated control voltage of 26V. Determine the motor transfer function.

NINE

Stability in linear servo systems

9.1. GENERAL

A system is defined as being *stable* if it will return to a state of
equilibrium in some definite amount of time after it has been subjected to
a disturbance. This time length usually has certain limits which are determined by the system's application.

9.2. SYSTEM RESPONSES

A simple closed-loop servo system using a synchro transmitter and
control transformer as transducers is shown in figure 9-1. The error
voltage from the CT is fed into an amplifier which controls the servo motor
which is driving a load and the rotor of the CT. The system transfer
function is also given.

Figure 9-2 shows the response curves for such a servo that has been
subjected to a *step-position* command. The original controlled output had
been on the *x*-line, and the step-position command now drives it to the
y-line; the system responds along one of the three curves, depending on the
damping.

Curve 1 shows the response of an underdamped system with its peak
overshoot, oscillation period and settling time. The *settling time* is the
time it takes for the system to come within the tolerance band by the fourth
time constant, or after 98 % change has resulted. In addition, the system
could hunt continuously. For proper operation of this servo, the feedback

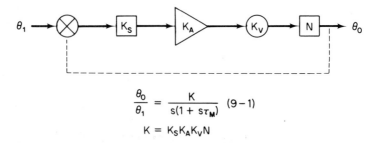

$$\frac{\theta_0}{\theta_1} = \frac{K}{s(1 + s\tau_M)} \quad (9-1)$$

$$K = K_S K_A K_V N$$

FIG. 9-1. A Simple Closed-loop System

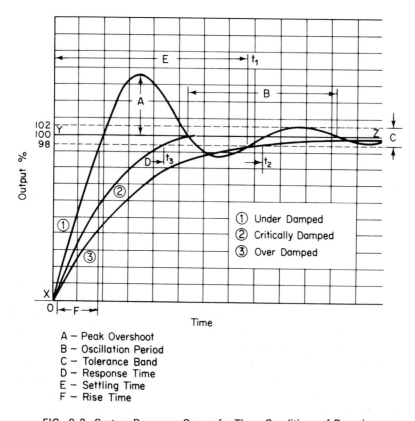

A — Peak Overshoot
B — Oscillation Period
C — Tolerance Band
D — Response Time
E — Settling Time
F — Rise Time

FIG. 9-2. System Response Curves for Three Conditions of Damping

voltage from the output opposes or subtracts from that of the reference input, *i.e.*, negative feedback; therefore, as the error increases, the restoring torque, which tends to reduce the error, also rises.

As the time lag between the system input and output becomes greater

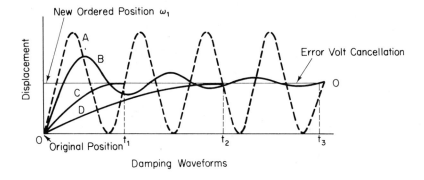

Damping Waveforms

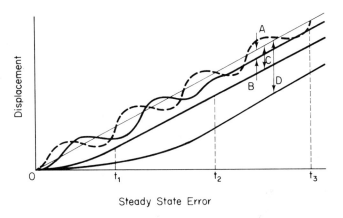

Steady State Error

A — Undamped
B — Underdamped
C — Critically Damped
D — Overdamped

FIG. 9-3. Comparisons of Steady State Errors and Restoring Torques for Different
Conditions of Damping

and greater—over one-half cycle—the feedback voltage from the output
transducer reverses polarity, and, instead of subtracting from the input, it
now adds to it, *i.e.*, positive feedback. Thus, the input to the amplifier and
thence to the motor drives the motor in the same direction as the input is
displaced. This means that the error is increased rather than decreased,
and, if it is allowed to build up, it will eventually saturate the system so
that it will oscillate continuously. Figures 9-3 and 9-4 show the steady-
state error and restoring torques that can exist for the different damping
ratios.

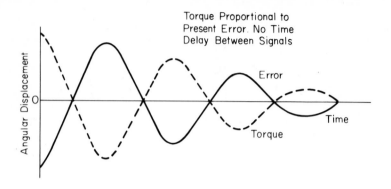

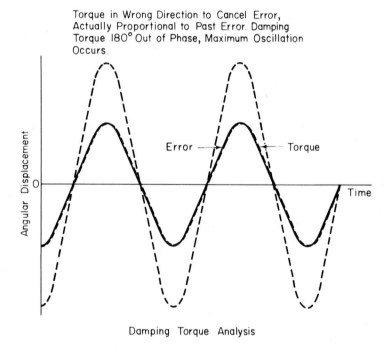

Damping Torque Analysis

FIG. 9-4. Analysis of Damping Torques and an Error Signal

In analyzing system performance, two questions can be asked:

1. How close can the output shaft be positioned in respect to the input
   shaft? The answer here depends on static and running friction and its
   damping effect as discussed in Chapter 8, p. 117. When the torque at

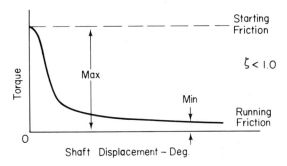

FIG. 9-5. Position Error for a Step Position Command

the output drops below that required to overcome the running-friction torque, a minimum positional error will exist. However, static friction is usually much larger than running friction so that when the input shaft is displaced again, a large difference in shaft position with a resultant large error voltage will be required to overcome the breakaway or stiction torque. Since this is the maximum positional error, this is the one usually considered in design calculations as the *minimum static error* of the system. Figure 9-5 shows this positional error. The term *position error constant*, K_{PE}, reflects this misalignment between input and output and can be found from

$$K_{PE} = \frac{E_e}{\theta}$$

where E_e is the error voltage and θ is the shaft displacement. Figure 9-6 shows the transient error curves for different vicsous-damped servos with different friction constants and damping ratios. It can be seen that the relative position error is about the same, but that the oscillations die out faster depending on the damping.

2. How close can the output shaft follow the input shaft if the input shaft rotates at a constant velocity? When the input shaft is started running at a constant speed, the output shaft will try to follow it. Again, because of system friction, there will be an opposing force which will cause the output to oscillate about the input shaft speed until it settles down. However, a difference in shaft positions will now exist, even though both are running at the same speed. This is called *steady-state velocity error* or *velocity lag error*; the value of this error is determined by the amplifier gain and the magnitude of the viscous friction (see equation 8-8). Figure 9-7 shows different viscous-damped servos with different damping ratios and friction constants for the

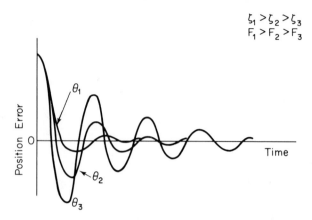

FIG. 9-6. Transient Error Responses for Different Damping Ratios—Step Position
Command

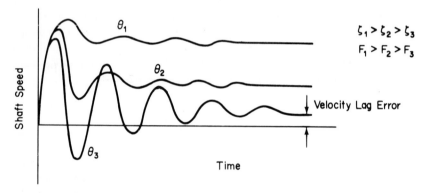

FIG. 9-7. Transient Error Responses for Different Damping Ratios—Step Velocity
Command

same step-velocity command. A comparison of these curves shows
that the servo with the largest steady-state error will have fewer
oscillations.

The actual damping of this system is related to the critical damping
in the following manner:

$$\text{Damping ratio (zeta)} = \frac{\text{actual damping}}{\text{critical damping}} \qquad \zeta = \frac{F}{2\sqrt{KJ}} \qquad (9\text{-}2)$$

The natural frequency at which the system will break into oscillations is

$$\text{Natural Frequency} = \omega_N = \sqrt{\frac{K}{J}} \ \text{rad/s} \qquad (9\text{-}3)$$

These equations show that the system gain, K, must be adjusted quite carefully because, when it is changed, the damping ratio varies inversely while the natural frequency varies directly. They also show that as the inertia, J, is decreased, it has the desirable effect of increasing ζ and ω_N. To improve damping, various methods of decreasing J and/or increasing F are used.

9.3. SERVO DAMPING

Most textbooks and manuals on servomechanism design derive their analysis on the assumption that the systems are linear and that the servo motor is linear. Idealized motor characteristics are shown in figure 9-8, and, from these, the designer makes his choice of components, defines any significant parameters, and estimates system performance with whatever experimental adjustment is required.

In most single-loop, second-order systems, the servo motor presents the most nonlinearity and the slope of the motor torque *vs.* the speed characteristic represents the motor damping as given by:

$$F = \frac{T_s}{S_0} \qquad (9\text{-}4)$$

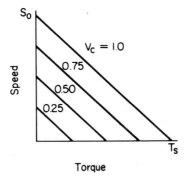

FIG. 9-8. Idealized Motor
Characteristics

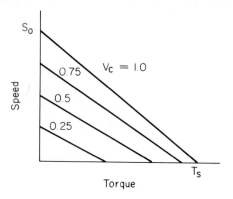

FIG. 9-9. Actual Motor Output with
Linear Characteristics

The damping is directly related to the velocity constant, K, and the motor time constant, τ_M, with both of these factors decreasing as the damping decreases. Damping also varies directly with stall torque and inversely with free speed.

Figure 9-9 shows the actual speed torque characteristics of a motor with a linear relationship. At low control voltage and low speeds, which represent static operation of a positioning servomechanism, the damping is about one-half the damping derived from the straight line, idealized curve. The actual slope is almost double what is expected when linearity is assumed. If the speed torque characteristic has a bulge, then damping varies with speed in a more complex manner. The larger the servo motor, the greater the curvature (see figure 9-10).

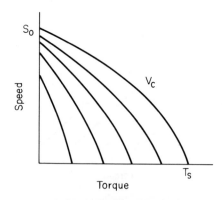

FIG. 9-10. Actual Motor Output with
Non-linear Characteristics

Using the actual curves, figure 9-10 leads to much better correlation between theory and experiment. The most important special condition occurs at low speed and low control voltage where damping is at a minimum and the tendency to oscillate is greatest. For slewing or steady operation at a specific speed, the damping associated with stability is taken as the slope at the actual operating point.

To obtain the parameters for equations 9-2 and 9-3 which are most suitable for a particular application, the servo designer has a number of damping techniques available. Some of these techniques are described below.

9.4. DAMPING METHODS

Sections 9.4(A) through 9.4(C) illustrate and describe different types of mechanical devices or networks that are used for stabilization purposes, while sections 9.5(A) through 9.5(E) show the changes in the block diagram and transfer function that occur when these methods are used.

INHERENT DAMPING. The following methods increase the natural damping of either ac or dc servo motors without adding mechanical complications:

1. reducing the skew of the rotor
2. reducing the inertia of the rotor
3. increasing the resistance of the rotor
4. using dc on the motor windings

Use of these techniques will allow the free speed of a certain six-pole, 400 Hz motor to be reduced from 6000 rpm to as low as 4500 rpm. However, reducing the rotor skew or using dc has disadvantages which are:

1. an increase in the starting voltage which decreases system sensitivity
2. a reduction in the slewing speed
3. an increase in power losses
4. a tendency to cause motor dither at system null

Reducing the inertia of the rotor increases the damping ratio and also increases the speed of response of the system.

VISCOUS OR VELOCITY DAMPING. Viscous and velocity or rate damping techniques are those in which the amount of damping is directly proportional to the speed of rotation of the motor. The damping signal is produced electrically from a transducer at the output. The signal is fed back into the closed-loop with a polarity that (1) makes an *increasing* error appear *larger*, and (2) makes a *decreasing* error appear *smaller*. The most commonly used methods are listed below with all the methods introducing velocity lag into the system, *i.e.*, a steady-state error exists between input and output.

1. Viscous damping is achieved by different devices.
   (a) Air or oil dashpots, friction discs, brakes, gear type devices, magnetic brakes, eddy current brakes, fluids containing magnetic particles, etc.

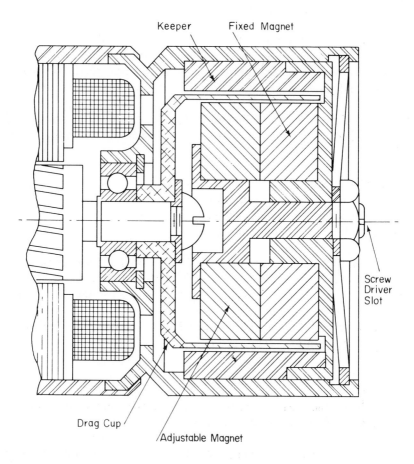

FIG. 9-11. Magnetic Viscous Damping Added to a Servo Motor (*Cedar Engineering Div., Control Data Corp.*)

(b) An aluminum drag cup rigidly connected to the motor shaft rotating in a magnetic field produced by two permanent magnets (see figure 9-11). One of the magnets is usually adjustable so the damping is adjustable.

These methods have little effect on starting voltage or torque, but they do increase the motor inertia and reduce the system slewing speed.

2. Velocity damping is obtained by means of feedback which comes from a tachometer-generator mounted integrally with the motor. If it is an ac tachometer, then it consists of a two-phase stator, a drag cup, and an adjustable core. One winding is excited from a reference source. The second winding has voltage induced in it because of the interaction of the drag cup and the reference winding. This voltage signal, which is proportional to the rate of change of the output, is fed to the amplifier in opposition to the error signal between the output and the input. The amplifier thus responds to the two signals, (1) due to the position error, and (2) due to a change in velocity. If it is a dc tachometer, then it may have a permanent magnet field with a wound rotor with the signal being dc, instead of ac (see figure 9-12). This method is very flexible because it allows a wide range of damping ratios over a wide range of speeds. The major disadvantages are:

(a) high cost
(b) introduction of noise
(c) an increase in motor inertia

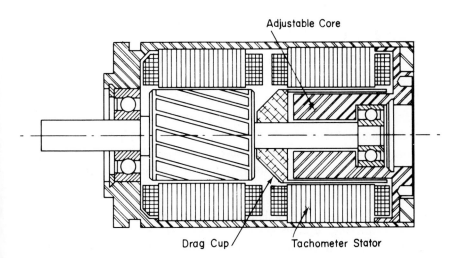

FIG. 9-12. A Motor-tachometer

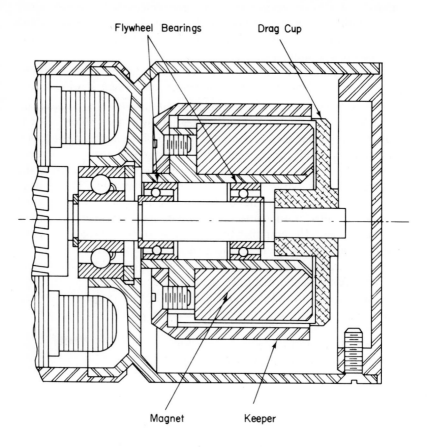

FIG. 9-13. Inertia Damper Added to a Servo Motor

(d) velocity lag

(e) introduction of temperature and frequency sensitive variable

3. Counter emf damping is produced when the counter emf of a dc servometer is used as the measure of speed. This generated voltage is fed directly into the amplifier but in opposition to the position error signal.

INERTIAL DAMPING.   Inertial damping is a form of viscous damping which does not introduce velocity lag. It consists of an aluminum drag cup rigidly connected to the motor shaft with a permanent magnet flywheel which is also on the shaft on ball bearings (see figure 9-13). The only time this drag cup has any effect is during acceleration. When the motor is running at a constant speed, the viscous coupling between the drag cup and the flywheel drives the flywheel at an essentially constant speed. This method does not affect motor performance very much, but it does introduce some errors during acceleration.

9.5.   MATHEMATICAL ANALYSIS

INHERENT AND VISCOUS DAMPING.   The transfer function of a linear ac servo motor can be written as in equation 9-5; J includes the inertia of the

$$\frac{\theta_M}{V_c} = \frac{K_T/F}{s[(J/F)s + 1]} \tag{9-5}$$

drag cup and the rotor, and F includes the viscous damping as well as the inherent damping.   F is determined from the slope of the characteristic curve and is given by equation 9-4.

TACHOMETER FEEDBACK.   When a tachometer is used for damping purposes, the block diagram in figure 9-1 is changed to that in figure 9-14. The transfer function for the inner loop is given in equation 9-6, with F in equation 9-5 being replaced by $F + K_A K_T K_G$.   J includes the inertia of the rotor and the drag cup.

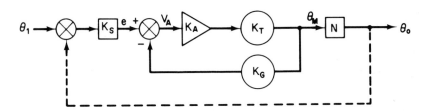

$$\frac{\theta_M}{V_A} = \frac{\dfrac{K_A K_T}{F + K_A K_T K_G}}{s\left(\dfrac{J}{F + K_A K_T K_G} s + 1\right)} \tag{9-6}$$

FIG. 9-14. Addition of a Tach Generator for Damping

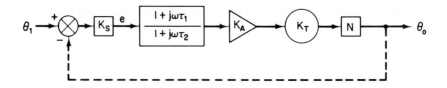

FIG. 9-15. Addition of a Corrective Network for Damping Purposes

INERTIAL DAMPING.   The transfer function of an inertial-damped motor can be written in the form given in equation 9-7; the values of J, F, J_d and F_d are determined by using the desired corner frequencies from a Bode plot. This type of motor responds to a step input with a large initial overshoot which is quickly attenuated. Critical damping is possible. Its most common application is in systems which require high velocity constants and low accelerations, but which cannot tolerate a velocity lag.

$$\frac{\theta_M}{V_c} = \frac{K_T/F}{s\left[\left(\dfrac{J}{F} + \dfrac{J_d}{F[(J_d/F_d)s + 1]}\right)s + 1\right]} \tag{9-7}$$

ERROR RATE DAMPING.   Error rate damping is also a form of damping which does not introduce velocity lag. It involves the use of components whose voltage output varies as the rate of change of error, that is during acceleration or deceleration periods. These are three or four terminal networks composed of different configurations of resistance and capacitance; they are called (1) *phase lag*, (2) *limited-phase lag*, (3) *limited-phase lead*, and (4) *lag-lead networks*. For a more complete description of each and its transfer function, see section 10.2. Figure 9-15 shows the addition of a limited-phase lag network in a closed-loop system.

THE CHARACTERISTIC EQUATION.   Let us look again at the equation 7-22 on page 104.

$$K_T\theta_1 = J\ddot{\theta}_0 + F\dot{\theta}_0 + K_T\theta_0 \quad \text{or} \quad K_T\theta_1 = J\frac{d^2}{dt^2}\theta_0 + F\frac{d}{dt}\theta_0 + K_T\theta_0 \tag{9-8}$$

which we now recognize as being in the quadratic form. Now let us equate the transient part to zero.

$$J\frac{d^2}{dt^2} + F\frac{d}{dt} + K = 0 \tag{9-9}$$

The roots of this equation, r_1 and r_2, will now be as follows with three possible solutions:

$$r_1, r_2 = \frac{-F \pm \sqrt{F^2 - 4KJ}}{2J} = -\frac{F}{2J} \pm \sqrt{\frac{F^2}{4J^2} - \frac{K}{J}} \qquad (9\text{-}10)$$

1. Negative, real and unequal roots. This solution leads to an over-damped system.

$$\frac{F^2}{4J^2} > \frac{K}{J} \quad \text{or} \quad \zeta = \frac{F}{2}\frac{1}{\sqrt{KJ}} > 1 \qquad (9\text{-}11)$$

2. Negative, real and equal roots. This solution leads to a critically damped system.

$$\frac{F^2}{4J^2} = \frac{K}{J} \quad \text{or} \quad \zeta = \frac{F}{2}\frac{1}{\sqrt{KJ}} = 1 \qquad (9\text{-}12)$$

3. Conjugate and complex with negative real parts. This solution leads to an underdamped system.

$$\frac{F^2}{4J^2} < \frac{K}{J} \quad \text{or} \quad \zeta = \frac{F}{2}\frac{1}{\sqrt{KJ}} < 1 \qquad (9\text{-}13)$$

Thus, for critical damping, the friction constant, F_C, should equal $2\sqrt{KJ}$. The ratio of actual damping to critical damping is denoted by zeta (ζ) and $\zeta = F/F_C = F/2\sqrt{KJ}$. The frequency at which the system will break into oscillation is called the natural frequency and is given by $W_N = \sqrt{K/J}$ in radians/second or $f_N = (1/(2\pi))(\sqrt{K/J})$ in hertz. The bandwidth of the system will now be the range of frequencies the system can follow over which the amplitude of the output stays above the half power point or above -3dB.

Some example problems will now illustrate the theory presented.

EXAMPLE 9-1

A viscous damped servo has a natural angular frequency of 15 rad/s. A step velocity command of 50 deg/s is introduced to the servo. Under the assumption that the servo is critically damped determine: (1) the steady-state error, (2) the damping time constant, and (3) the maximum step-velocity command that will limit the steady state error to 0.5°.

1. $e_{s.s.} = \dfrac{2\zeta}{\omega_N} \times \text{S.V.C.} = \dfrac{2 \times 1.0 \times 50 \text{ deg/s}}{15 \text{ rad/sec}} = 6.66°$ ANS

2. $\tau = \dfrac{1}{\zeta\omega_N} = \dfrac{1}{1.0 \times 15 \text{ rad/s}} = 0.066 \text{ s}$ ANS

3. $\text{S.V.C.} = \dfrac{e_{s.s.}.\omega_N}{2\zeta} = \dfrac{0.5° \times 15 \text{ rad/s}}{2 \times 1.0} = 3.75°/s$ ANS

EXAMPLE 9-2

A mechanical position servo is shown in the following diagram. The load is an instrument pen recorder with the following specifications:

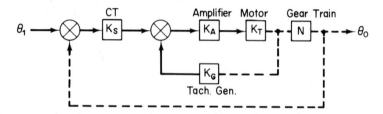

Specs: (1) Rate of pen movement—50 deg/s.
(2) Threshold—<0.12°
(3) Scale factor—415 mV/deg approximately
(4) Damping ratio—>0.4
(5) Input transducer signal—11.8V line-to-line
(6) Power supply—260V 400 Hz.

The following synchro and motor will be used: Size 8 CT 411mV/deg sensitivity 11.8V and a size 8 motor with the following specs: $T_S = 0.15$ oz-in; $S_0 = 6000$ rpm; $V_c = 26V$; $J = 0.48$ gm-cm^2; and starting voltage 10% of V_C.

We will now determine the following things:

(a) Gear Ratio $\dfrac{\text{Pen}_{\text{Rate}} \times 60 \text{ s}}{360°} = \text{rpm}$

$$\text{rpm} = \dfrac{50 \text{ deg/s} \times 60 \text{ s}}{360°} = 8.3 \text{ rpm}$$

$$\text{Gear Ratio} = \dfrac{S_0}{\text{rpm}_{\text{PEN}}} = \dfrac{6000}{8.3} = 723 \quad \text{or} \quad N = \dfrac{1}{725}$$

(b) $V_{dead \atop band} = 0.12° \times 411$ mV/deg $= 0.049$V

(c) Amplifier Gain K_A $K_A = \dfrac{V_c \times \%V_{S.T.}}{V_{D.B.}} = \dfrac{26 \times 0.1}{0.049} = 53$

(d) CT Gain $K_S = 57.3°V_{SEN.} = 57.3° \times 0.411 = 23.6$ V/rad
  K_S

(e) Torque Constant K_T $K_T = \dfrac{T_S}{V_S} = \dfrac{0.15 \text{ oz-in}}{26V} = 0.0058$ oz-in/V

(f) Overall Gain $K = K_S K_A K_T N$
  K
$$= 23.6\text{V/rad} \times 53 \times 0.0058 \text{ oz-in/V} \times \frac{1}{725}$$
$$= 0.01 \text{ oz-in/V}$$

(g) Damping Characteristic $F = \dfrac{T_s}{S_0} = \dfrac{0.15 \text{ oz-in}}{6000 \text{ rpm}} \times \dfrac{60}{2\pi}$
  F
$$= 2.39 \times 10^{-4} \text{ oz-in/rad/s}$$

(h) Velocity Constant K_V $K_V = \dfrac{K_T}{F} = \dfrac{5.8 \times 10^{-3} \text{ oz-in/V}}{2.39 \times 10^{-4} \text{ oz-in/rad/s}}$
$$= 24.3 \text{ rad/s/V}$$

(i) $\zeta = \dfrac{F}{2\sqrt{KJ}} = \dfrac{2.39 \times 10^{-4} \text{ oz-in/rad/s}}{2\sqrt{1.0 \times 10^{-2} \text{ oz-in/V} \times 6.8 \times 10^{-6} \text{ oz-in-s}^2}} J$

$= 0.48$ gm-cm^2

$= \dfrac{0.48}{7.062} = 0.068 \times 10^{-4}$ oz-in-s^2

$= \dfrac{2.39 \times 10^{-4} \text{ oz-in/rad/s}}{2 \times 2.61 \times 10^{-4} \text{ oz-in-s}}$

$= 0.46$

(j) Transfer Function $\tau = \dfrac{J}{F} = \dfrac{6.8 \times 10^{-6} \text{ oz-in-s}^2}{2.39 \times 10^{-4} \text{ oz-in/rad/s}} = 0.0285$ s

$$\text{T.F.} = \dfrac{K_V}{S(1 + \tau s)} = \dfrac{24.3}{S(1 + 0.9285s)}$$

$$= \dfrac{24.3 \times 35.1}{s(35.1 + s)} = \dfrac{852}{s(s + 35.1)}$$

If this damping ratio, (ζ), is not large enough, then tachometer feedback can be adjusted to bring it above some minimum value. Reducing the inertia of the motor will also do this, *i.e.*, using a motor with a higher free speed and a lower moment of inertia.

QUESTIONS AND PROBLEMS

1. A feedback potentiometer has a total travel of 350°. Determine the transfer function if the supply voltage is 45V.

2. Give a clear and concise definition of the following terms:
   (a) natural frequency   (f) phase lag
   (b) deadband   (g) velocity-lag error
   (c) zeta   (h) position error
   (d) settling time   (i) error rate damping
   (e) velocity damping

3. A servo has a natural frequency of 7.5 Hz and a moment of inertia of 0.308 oz-in-s². What is the torque gradient in oz-in/deg? If the damping ratio is equal to 0.65, what is F_C in oz-in-s/rad?

4. A servo has a torque gradient of $K_T = 10$ oz-in/deg. The moment of inertia is 0.624 oz-in-s². What is the natural frequency?

5. The friction constant, F, of the servo problem 4 is 18 oz-in/rad/s. What is the damping ratio, zeta?

6. A viscous-damped servo driving a position follow up system has a natural angular frequency of 12 rad/s with an input velocity of 40 deg/s. Determine:
   (a) the steady-state error for critical damping when zeta equals 1.0
   (b) the steady-state error when zeta equals 0.8
   (c) the damping time constant for problem 6a
   (d) the damping time constant for problem 6b

7. A viscous-damped servo has a natural frequency of 10 rad/s and a zeta of 0.8. A step-velocity command of 80 deg/s is introduced. Determine:
   (a) the steady-state error
   (b) the maximum displacement of the output during the transient period

8. Repeat problem 7 for a zeta of 0.9.

9. For the servo in problem 6, calculate the proportional change in zeta that will reduce the steady-state error for critical damping by 20%, *i.e.*, to 0.8 of the value found in problem 6a.

10. The torque gradient of a servo motor is 12 oz-in/deg. It has a natural frequency of 6 Hz. What is the moment of inertia in oz-in-sec^2?

11. A positioning servo system uses synchros as error detectors. The system has the following load requirements: (1) rate of moment = 50 deg/s, and (2) a deadband of 1.0°. Using the motor of Example 8-1, determine the following, assuming that the motor will start the load with 10% voltage. Also assume that the CT has a sensitivity of 415 mV/deg.

(a) the gear ratio
(b) the amplifier gain
(c) the overall gain, K
(d) the damping factor

TEN

Frequency response in servo systems

10.1. ANALYSIS USING NYQUIST PLOTS

To test a servo such as that mentioned in Chapter 7, many engineers apply a step-position command to the input and then measure or calculate the ensuing overshoot, errors, rise time, settling time, etc. However, many engineers prefer to apply a sinusoidal command and then to measure the loop gain and phase lag for a range of input frequencies.

To do this, the loop is opened at the error detector, R is reduced to zero, and a sinusoidal command of low frequency and low constant voltage is applied in place of the error singal (see figure 10-1).

The measurements now consist of the voltage at F and the phase angle by which F lags E. These readings are taken for a range of frequencies so that a polar plot of the feedback voltage can be plotted *vs.* phase angle. To find the gain, the ratio of F to R must be used under closed-loop conditions. This is done by reconnecting F to the error detector so that $E = R - F$ or $R = F + E$. Since E is a constant value, the length of vector R on the plot is the vector sum of a $-E$ and a varying

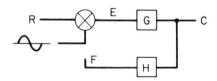

FIG. 10-1. Opening of a Feedback loop

EXAMPLE 10-1

Nyquist Plot

$$\frac{C}{R} = \frac{10}{(1 + j\omega\tau_1)(1 + j\omega\tau_2)}$$

$$\frac{C}{R} = \frac{10}{(1 + j0.05\omega)(1 + j0.1\omega)}$$

$$F = \frac{10}{A_1 A_2} \qquad A_1 = (1^2 + (0.05\omega)^2)^{\frac{1}{2}}$$
$$A_2 = (1^2 + (0.1\omega)^2)^{\frac{1}{2}}$$

$$\theta_T = \theta_1 + \theta_2 \qquad \theta_T = -\text{Tan}^{-1}\, 0.05\omega - \text{Tan}^{-1}\, 0.1\omega$$

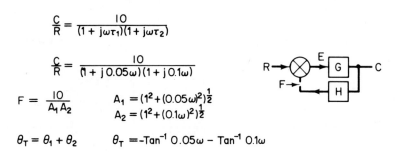

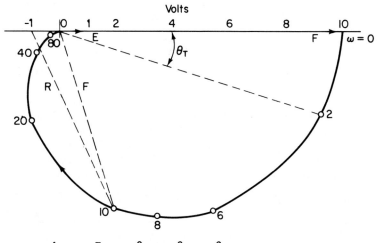

ω Rad/Sec	f Hz	F Volts	θ_1 Deg	θ_2 Deg	θ_T Deg
2	0.32	9.7	−6	−11	−17
6	0.96	8.2	−17	−31	−48
8	1.28	7.2	−22	−39	−61
10	1.6	6.3	−27	−45	−72
20	3.2	3.2	−45	−63	−108
40	6.4	1.1	−63	−76	−139
80	12.8	0.3	−76	−83	−159
200	32	0.1	−84	−87	−171

F. Vector E is now drawn so that its tail is at a −1. Now any line drawn from the −1 point to any point on the polar plot equals R. Example 10-1 clearly illustrates how this is done.

The ratio of F/R is now considered for three cases:

1. When F is smaller than R, the feedback lags the input by an angle up to 90°.

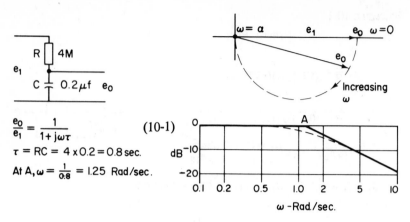

$$\frac{e_0}{e_1} = \frac{1}{1 + j\omega\tau} \qquad (10\text{-}1)$$

$\tau = RC = 4 \times 0.2 = 0.8\,\text{sec.}$

At A, $\omega = \frac{1}{0.8} = 1.25\,\text{Rad/sec.}$

FIG. 10-2. Phase Lag Network

2. When F is 1.414 times larger than R, the angle of lag is 135°.

3. When F is about four times larger than R, the angle of lag is about 180°.

The criterion that determines whether a system will be stable or unstable is called the Nyquist criterion. It is as follows:

1. If the curve passes to the right of the -1 point, then the system is absolutely stable.

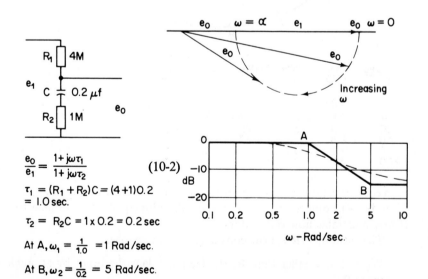

$$\frac{e_0}{e_1} = \frac{1 + j\omega\tau_1}{1 + j\omega\tau_2} \qquad (10\text{-}2)$$

$\tau_1 = (R_1 + R_2)C = (4+1)0.2$
$= 1.0\,\text{sec.}$

$\tau_2 = R_2C = 1 \times 0.2 = 0.2\,\text{sec}$

At A, $\omega_1 = \frac{1}{1.0} = 1\,\text{Rad/sec.}$

At B, $\omega_2 = \frac{1}{0.2} = 5\,\text{Rad/sec.}$

FIG. 10-3. Limited Phase Lag Network

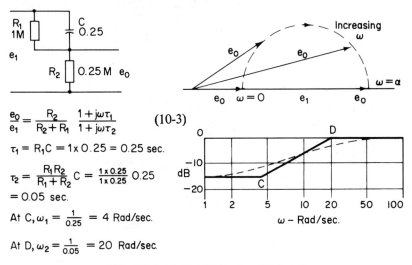

$$\frac{e_0}{e_1} = \frac{R_2}{R_2 + R_1} \frac{1 + j\omega\tau_1}{1 + j\omega\tau_2} \qquad (10\text{-}3)$$

$$\tau_1 = R_1 C = 1 \times 0.25 = 0.25 \text{ sec.}$$

$$\tau_2 = \frac{R_1 R_2}{R_1 + R_2} C = \frac{1 \times 0.25}{1 \times 0.25} \, 0.25$$
$$= 0.05 \text{ sec.}$$

$$\text{At } C, \omega_1 = \frac{1}{0.25} = 4 \text{ Rad/sec.}$$

$$\text{At } D, \omega_2 = \frac{1}{0.05} = 20 \text{ Rad/sec.}$$

FIG. 10-4. Limited Phase Lead Network

2. If the curve passes through the -1 point, then continuous oscillation will result, and the system is absolutely unstable.

3. If the curve passes to the left of the -1 point, then the system will be unstable with the gain determining the instability.

10.2.   NYQUIST PLOT CORRECTION

The upper limits for useful stability is in the range of 1.5 to 2.0 for the F/R ratio.   Corrective networks such as those shown in figures 10-2 through 10-5 change the gain of the system, and thus the shape of the polar plot so that the -1 point is no longer encircled.   Figure 10-6 shows a system that has been stabilized in a conditional sense by a *Notch* network; figure 10-7 shows the different types of servos with their transfer functions and Nyquist plot corrections.

10.3.   ANALYSIS USING BODE PLOTS

A control system consists of devices connected by signal paths.   Each device may change the magnitude of its input signal and the *time* of this signal depending on the frequency of the input signal.   A dc signal can be attenuated in size but not in time, while an ac signal can be attenuated in both size and time (phase).

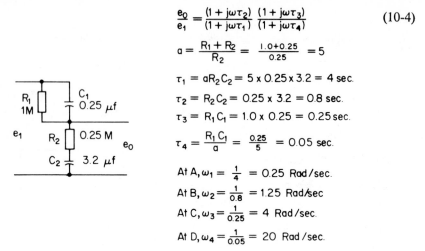

$$\frac{e_0}{e_1} = \frac{(1 + j\omega\tau_2)}{(1 + j\omega\tau_1)} \frac{(1 + j\omega\tau_3)}{(1 + j\omega\tau_4)} \qquad (10\text{-}4)$$

$$a = \frac{R_1 + R_2}{R_2} = \frac{1.0 + 0.25}{0.25} = 5$$

$$\tau_1 = aR_2C_2 = 5 \times 0.25 \times 3.2 = 4 \text{ sec.}$$

$$\tau_2 = R_2C_2 = 0.25 \times 3.2 = 0.8 \text{ sec.}$$

$$\tau_3 = R_1C_1 = 1.0 \times 0.25 = 0.25 \text{ sec.}$$

$$\tau_4 = \frac{R_1C_1}{a} = \frac{0.25}{5} = 0.05 \text{ sec.}$$

At A, $\omega_1 = \frac{1}{4} = 0.25$ Rad/sec.

At B, $\omega_2 = \frac{1}{0.8} = 1.25$ Rad/sec

At C, $\omega_3 = \frac{1}{0.25} = 4$ Rad/sec.

At D, $\omega_4 = \frac{1}{0.05} = 20$ Rad/sec.

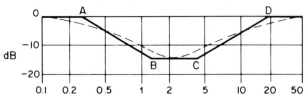

FIG. 10-5. Lag Lead (Notch) Network

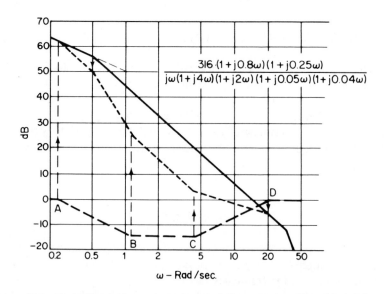

$$\frac{316 \cdot (1 + j0.8\omega)(1 + j0.25\omega)}{j\omega(1 + j4\omega)(1 + j2\omega)(1 + j0.05\omega)(1 + j0.04\omega)}$$

ω – Rad/sec.

FIG. 10-6. Notch Network Used to Stabilize a System (Conditionally)

154

Servo Type	Type 0	Type 1	Type 2
Used As	Regulator of Level or Quantity	Position Control No Standstill Error	Position Control No Velocity Error
Start – Stop Motors	0	1	2
Typical Transf. Function	$\dfrac{300}{(1+j\omega\tau_1)(1+j\omega\tau_2)(1+j\omega\tau_3)}$	$\dfrac{300}{j\omega\,(1+j\omega\tau_1)(1+j\omega\tau_2)}$	$\dfrac{300}{j\omega^2(1+j\omega\tau_1)(1+j\omega\tau_2)}$
Nyquist Plot Correction	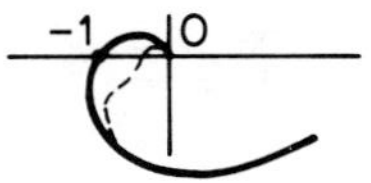	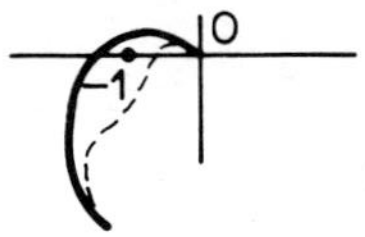	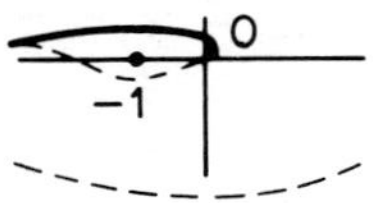
Stabilization	Not Difficult	Requires Care	Needs Precise Corrective Design
Slope on Bode Plot	0	–1 Unit Slope 20 dB/Decade	–2 Unit Slope 40 dB/Decade
Error	Small Steady State Error	Velocity Lag	Acceleration Lag

FIG. 10-7. Types of Servos and Nyquist Correction

The change in size between the input and output is called the gain or amplification of the device or system, and it may be designated by the letter K with the proper subscript or by the letter G. The change in the *time* of the signal is simply the number of degrees by which the output differs from the input or by how much the output lags the input. This time change is usually called the *phase angle* or *phase difference* (*lag* or *lead*), and it is given in degrees. It is considered a positive phase difference when the output leads the input and negative when the output lags the input.

The frequency response of any device or system is the table of values of K or G and the phase angle, θ, which results when a sinusoidal test signal is varied over a range of frequencies, usually from 0.1 to 10 or 20 or more hertz. These values may be plotted as two graphs on the same paper and are known as *Bode plots*. It is normal practice in the Bode plot or diagram to use a vertical linear scale for the gain and phase angle and a horizontal log decade scale for the frequency (semilog paper). The gain of the device or system is converted to decibels as A or M (dB) = $20 \log_{10} K$ or G, thus allowing one to use the linear scale. The horizontal log decade scale is the frequency, ω, in radians per second.

In the analysis of device or servo operation, two methods are used: one is by experiment and the other is an analytical procedure. In the experimental method, a sinusoidal signal from a servo analyzer or function generator is applied to the input of a system, and the output is measured. The ratio of the output to the input is determined, and the gain in decibels is computed. A dual-beam oscilloscope can show the relationship as well as the phase angle. However, this method may be difficult; therefore, the analytical method is used because it is simpler and easier.

In the analytical method, the mathematical equation, *i.e.*, transfer function, that represents the system is used. The transfer function of a device or system is usually given by an equation ranging from a constant, to an algebraic relation, to a differential equation. If the system's transfer function is a differential equation, then the use of LaPlace transforms will change this into an algebraic equation. LaPlace transforms allow one to go from the time domain to the frequency domain. This operational method transforms a differential equation from a function of time f(t) to an algebraic equation F(s) which is a function containing the LaPlace operator $s = a + j\omega$, consisting of a real portion a and an imaginary portion $j\omega$. However, to make the Bode plot it is necessary to change the operator s to frequency in radians per second or hertz, and this is done by simply using the real portion a and the imaginary portion $j\omega$.

Logarithmic values are used because of the ease with which multiplication and division of numbers are handled. For example, if two devices are cascaded, then the overall gain is the product of the individual gains $A_1 A_2$, but, in decibels, the gain is the sum of $dBA_1 + dBA_2$. If the transfer function has a reciprocal such as $1/(1 + j\omega\tau)$, then the gain in decibels is the negative value of db$\omega\tau$. The logarithm of the frequency, ω, is not quite exact since the dimensions of ω are radians per second. Some texts use ω/ω_0 or $\omega\tau$ as the semilog scale for frequency, but, in this text, we will state that ω represents a dimensionless number that has the numerical value of frequency in radians per second.

10.4. BODE PLOT CONSTRUCTION

A Bode diagram can be plotted for any transfer function with this function representing any of the following factors:

1. K—a constant.
2. $j\omega$ or any power of $j\omega$, such as $(j\omega)^2$.
3. $1 + j\omega\tau$ or any power of $1 + j\omega\tau$, such as $(1 + j\omega\tau)^2$.
4. $1 + j\omega K_1 + (j\omega)^2 K_2$ (This is a quadratic factor with complex roots and it will not be covered here.)
5. Factors 2 and 3 give a *leading* function. The reciprocal of either of these, which is the usual thing, gives a *lagging* function.

When the diagram is actually constructed, the following things can be noted:

1. Straight lines are used to approximate all magnitude curves.
2. Semilog paper is used.
3. Values of ω are plotted on the abscissa, but the graph is log ω because of the log divisions.
4. The ordinate is also a log value of gain, dBA. Therefore, the frequency curve is a log-log plot.
5. The phase angle or phase shift curve has the same horizontal axis divisions as the gain curve; thus, its values always correspond to the gain values at any frequency.
6. When functions are multiplied, their phase angles are added.

When considering any constant, K, we find that it is plotted as a straight horizontal line with 20 log K or KdB being a constant. If K equals 1.0, then 20 log 1 equals 0, and the line falls on the 0dB-line. K causes no phase shift, so the phase angle is 0°.

The second factor, $j\omega$, has magnitude and phase angles. The value of j is 90°, j^2 is 180°, j^3 is 270°, etc.; ω is the distance up or down the j-axis. The log gain is in decibels and equals 20 log jω, or 20 log (jω)^2 which equals 40 log |jω|. Each jω turn has an upward sloping line at 20dB/decade, thus (jω)^2 slopes at 40dB/decade, etc. If the term is 1/jω, then 20 log |1/jω| equals 20 log (jω)$^{-1}$ which gives a negative slope of −20dB/decade.

The third factor, 1 + j$\omega\tau$, can be analyzed in the following manner: τ is the time constant and ω is the frequency variable. If ω is much less than 1/τ, then j$\omega\tau$ becomes quite small (negligible), and 1 + j$\omega\tau$ becomes almost 1. Thus, at low frequencies, the function on the diagram is K equals 1 with a phase angle of 0°. If ω is much greater than 1/τ, j$\omega\tau$ is very much larger than 1, and 1 + j$\omega\tau$ becomes almost equal to j$\omega\tau$. On a Bode diagram, jω and j$\omega\tau$ plot the same except for a parallel shift of the log gain line. Thus, j$\omega\tau$ has a slope of 20dB/decade and a phase angle of 90°. When this line is drawn, we will find that it intersects with the K-line at the point called the corner frequency or breakpoint where 1/τ becomes equal to 1 (see example 10-2).

EXAMPLE 10-2
Let us analyze the following function:

$$\frac{C}{R} = \frac{K}{j\omega(1 + j\omega\tau)} = \frac{20}{j\omega(1 + j0.25\omega)} = \frac{20}{j\omega[1 + j(\omega/4)]}$$

which has three elements. Each of these elements can be plotted separately on a Bode diagram, and then their log magnitude values must be added. For small values of ω, the element 1/(1 + j0.25ω) becomes 1/1 or 1, and the total function is 20/jω which has a slope of −20dB/decade.

In order to start the line, one point is needed so 20 log K/jω = 20 log K/ω, when K = 20 we have 20 log K/K = 20 log 1 = 0. *Therefore, the initial slope either goes through the point ω = K on the 0dB line or would go through this point if the line were extended.* This is the *anchor point* in all asymptotic or straight line Bode diagram plots with jω in the denominator.

The second line comes from the function 1 + j0.25W because of very large values of jω which effectively "swamp" the 1 in the function. If ω = 100, then 1 + j0.25ω becomes 1 + j25, the absolute value of which is |1^2 + 25^2|. At these high values of ω, 1/(1 + j0.25ω) approaches 1/jω and the total function is (20/jω)(1/jω) = 20/(jω)^2 which has a slope of −40dB/decade and starts at the breakpoint. In this case, the breakpoint is where 1 + jω/4 becomes 1 + j1 which is when ω = 4. Therefore, from the intersection of the −20dB/decade line and the frequency ω = 4, the final line is drawn at a slope of −40dB/decade (see figure 10-8).

The phase shift curve can also be plotted on the Bode diagram. For this function, the gain K = 20 is a constant at 0°, so it does not affect the phase plot. The phase shift actually starts at 90° because of the single jω

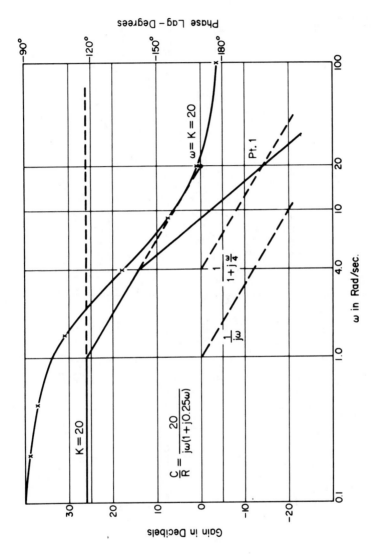

FIG. 10-8. A Bode Diagram of the Function

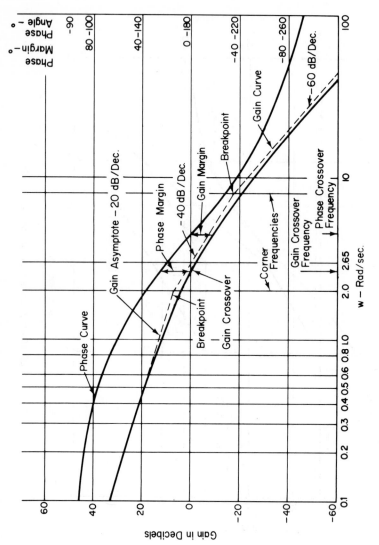

FIG. 10-9. A Typical Bode Diagram

160

term; thus, when $\omega = 0$, we have $20/j\omega$, but 20 does not affect the phase, so $1/j\omega = 1/90° = -90°$. The term $1 + j\omega/4$ combines with the single term $1/j\omega$ to give angles between 90° and 180°. At high frequencies, we have $(1/j\omega)[1/(1 + j\omega/4)] = 1/(j\omega)^2$ which is $1/180° = -180°$. See figure 10-8.

EXAMPLE 10-3
Let $\omega = 20$ then

$$\frac{C}{R} = \frac{20}{j20(1 + J20/4)} = \frac{20}{j20(1 + J5)}$$

$$dBA = 20 \log 20 - 20 \log 20 - 20 \log 5$$
$$= 26.02 - 26.02 - 13.98 = -13.98 \text{ (see Pt. 1)}$$

$$\theta = 0° - 90° - \tan^{-1}5 = 0° - 90° - 78.5° = -168.5°$$

10.5.   SUMMARY

The following statements can now be made about the Bode plot in terms of stability.

1. If the phase shift angle is 180° or higher at unity gain (0dB), then the system may be completely unstable when the loop is closed.

2. The closer the slope of the gain curve is to a -20dB/decade slope when the plot crosses the unity gain (0dB) line, the more stable the system will be.

3. The *gain crossover frequency* is the frequency at which the gain curve crosses the unity gain (0dB) line. The phase angle is noted at this point, and, if it is a negative 180° or higher, then the system will be inherently unstable.

4. To insure stability, the phase angle at the gain crossover frequency is kept well under $-180°$, the amount under is called the *phase margin*. A phase margin of 40° (phase angle: $-180° + 40° = -140°$) to 60° (phase angle: $-180° + 60° = -120°$) is desired for most servos.

5. Finally, if it is impossible to get 180° phase shift or if such a phase shift will occur with extremely low gain, then the system will be inherently stable.

Figure 10-9 shows a typical Bode diagram with the above information clearly labeled.

EXAMPLE 10-4
The following is the open-loop diagram of a servo system.

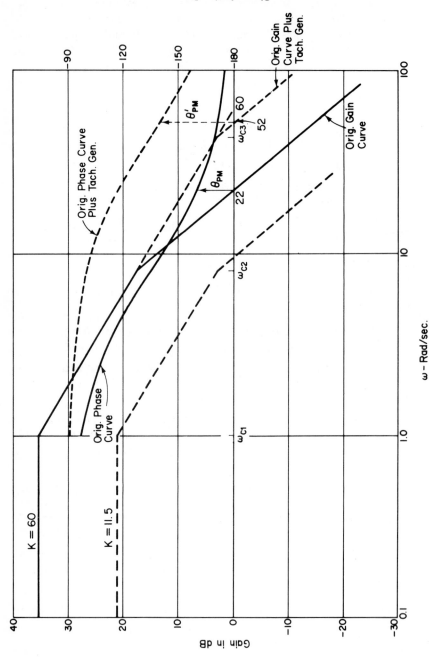

Phase Angle - Deg.

ω - Rad/sec.

Gain in dB

1. Write the open-loop transfer function in frequency response form.
2. Calculate the phase angle for $\omega = 2, 4, 8, 20, 40, 80$ rad/s.
3. Draw the Bode diagram-gain and phase plot on 3 cy. semilog paper (1) start with $\omega = 0.1$ (2) dB scale from -30 to $+40$ for major divisions. Show the anchor point.
4. What is the phase margin?
5. What is the gain crossover frequency?
6. Determine from the Bode plot the gain this system will have for a signal frequency of 30 rad/s. Check by calculation.
7. As the gain of this system is reduced it becomes less and less unstable. At what gain in dB and signal frequency will it become or start to become more stable? Determine the value in K that corresponds to this point.
8. If you did not want to reduce gain then what could be done to stabilize the system? Explain how and why.

Solution:

1. In order to write the open-loop function, it will be necessary to change the LaPlace operator "S" to the frequency form of "jω" and also to calculate the time constant tau (τ). Thus

$$\tau = \frac{J}{F} = \frac{0.3 \text{ oz-in-sec}^2}{2.4 \text{ oz-in/rad/sec}} = 0.125 \text{ sec}$$

$$\frac{\theta_0}{e} = \frac{K_A K_V}{s^2\tau + s} = \frac{K_A K_V}{s(\tau s + 1)}$$

and $s = j\omega$ so

$$\frac{\theta_0}{e} = \frac{K_A K_V}{j\omega(1 + j\omega\tau)} = \frac{5 \times 12}{j\omega(1 + j\omega 0.125)} = \frac{60}{j\omega(1 + j0.125\omega)}$$

Normalizing the equation gives

$$\frac{\theta_0}{e} = \frac{60}{j\omega[1 + j(\omega/8)]} \quad \text{ANS}$$

2. $\dfrac{60}{j\omega[1 + j(\omega/8)]}$

$\tan^{-1} j\omega = -90°$, $\tan^{-1} j(\omega/8)$ at $\omega = 2$, $\theta = -14°$, $\theta_T = -90° + -14° = -104°$

ω	θ_T
2	$-104°$
4	$-117°$
8	$-135°$
20	$-158°$
40	$-169°$
80	$-174°$

3. Anchor point $= \dfrac{K_A K_V}{j\omega} = \dfrac{60}{j\omega} = 60$ rad/s

Corner frequencies:

$$\omega_{C1} = j\omega = 1 \qquad \omega_{C2} = j\frac{\omega}{8} = 8$$

4. Phase margin θ_{PM} (solid curves) at a gain of 0dB

$$180° + (-160°) = 20° \quad \text{ANS}$$

5. Gain crossover frequency $\omega_{G.C.} = 22$ rad/s.

6. W $= 30$ rad/s from curve gain in dB $= -5.5$
   dB$_{cal.}$ $= 20 \log 60 - 20 \log 30 - 20 \log (30/8) = 35.6 - 29.5 - 11.5 = -5.4$ CK.

7. System stable at a $\theta_{PM} = 40° + \therefore$ from graph $\omega = 9.6$ rad/s with $K = 11.5$ or 21dB (see construction).

8. A tach. generator could be added (see example 9-2) and then have the output attenuated so that the viscous damping will be increased by a factor of as much as 5 or 6. Thus, let $F_{TG} = 12$ oz-in/rad/s and $J_{TG} = 0.03$ oz-in-s². The tach. generator inertia and viscous friction will add to those of the servo motor (see equation 9-6) where $K_A K_T K_G = F_{TG}$ and $J = J_M + J_{TG}$. Therefore a new time constant must be calculated and a new transfer function written.

$$\tau' = \frac{0.3 + 0.03}{2.4 + 12.0} = \frac{0.33}{14.4} = 0.023 \text{ s}$$

and

$$\frac{\theta_0}{e} = \frac{60}{j\omega(1 + j0.023\omega)} = \frac{60}{j\omega[1 + j(\omega/43.5)]} \quad \text{so} \quad \omega_{C3} = 43.5$$

The new phase lag points are now $-92°$, $-95°$, $-100°$, $-115°$, $-133°$, $-151°$, which shifts the phase curve up and to the right. The new gain curve is shown by the dotted line extension with a new corner frequency at ω_{C3}. The new crossover frequency is 52 rad/s. The new phase margin $\theta'_{PM} = 180° + (-140°) = 40°$, which is acceptable.

PROBLEMS

1. An amplidyne voltage regulator is wired according to the following diagram.

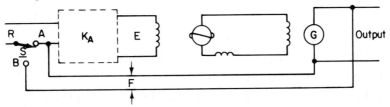

The amplidyne has the following parameters: 3KW, 125V, 1800 rpm. Quadrature field $= R_q = 1.4$ ohms; $L_q = 9.138$ henries. Control field $R_f = 1000$ ohms, $L_f = 36$ henries. Gain between E and F is 10 at $\omega = 0$. The generator field $R_f = 75$ ohm, $L_f = 38$ henries. The amplifier resistance can be taken as 1200 ohm. Consider the system as having three time constants, $T_1 =$ generator field, $T_2 =$ amplifier quadrature field, $T_3 =$ amplifier and amplidyne control field. Assuming that there is a 1.0V input at E, calculate the voltage at F and the phase angle for input frequencies of $\omega = 0, 1, 2, 3, 4, 5, 7.5, 10, 15, 20, 30$ and 40.

Open Loop—Switch S at position A
(a) Assuming that there is a 1.0V input at E, calculate the voltage at F and the phase lag in degrees for the following values of ω: $\omega = 0, 1, 2, 3, 4, 5, 7.5, 10, 15, 20, 30$ and 40.
(b) Plot the results as a Nyquist plot on graph paper.
(c) Determine if the regulator will be stable or unstable when the loop is closed.

Closed Loop—Switch S at position B
(a) If the gain is increased so that F becomes equal to or greater than E (at the 180° position), what will happen to system operation?

(b) If the plotted curve passed exactly through the -1 point, what would be true about the ratio of F to R? What is true about the stability?

2. The servo system that is shown in the following figure has a magnetic amplifier that has a time delay of $\tau = 0.05$ seconds. Using a Bode diagram, find the frequency where the open loop has a phase lag of $180°$, and also determine the amplifier gain, K_A, so that the overall gain is 1.0 at this frequency (stability limit).

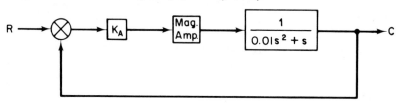

3. Plot the Bode diagram for $K = 2.5$, $K = 15$, and $K = 25$.

4. Plot the Bode diagram for (a) $(j\omega)^2$, (b) $(j\omega)^4$, and (c) $(j\omega)^3/(j\omega)^2$.

5. Plot the Bode diagram for (a) $1/(j\omega)^3$, (b) $1/(j\omega)^2$, and (c) $(j\omega)/(j\omega)^3$.

6. Plot the Bode diagram for the function $1/(1 + 0.1j\omega)$ by calculating gain and phase points for $\omega = 0.5, 2, 5, 8, 10, 12, 15, 20, 25, 40$ and 100.

7. Plot the Bode diagram for the function $20/[(1 + 0.1j\omega)j\omega]$.
   (a) Find gain and phase shift at a signal of 100 rad/s.
   (b) If C equals $1\mu\mu f$, find R to give the above function with an amplifier gain of 20.

8. Plot the Bode diagram for the function $15/[j\omega(1 + 0.5j\omega)]$.

9. Plot the Bode diagram for the function $15/[s^2(1 + 0.125s)]$.
   (a) Find gain and phase shift at a signal of $\omega = 2.0$, 15 and 20.
   (b) Find the gain crossover frequency, and the phase crossover frequency.
   (c) What is the phase margin? the gain margin?
   (d) Can this system be stabilized?

10. Plot the Bode diagram for the following system.

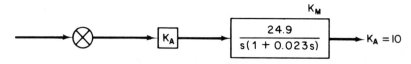

(a) Plot the Bode diagram of K_M only, K_A only, and K_A and K_M.
(b) What is bandwidth of K_M? K_A and K_M?

(c) What is the phase margin? gain margin?
(d) What is the phase crossover frequency? gain crossover frequency?
(e) Determine K_V.
(f) Identify K_A and K_M.
(g) If F is equal to 21.75 oz-in/rad/s, find J.

11. The following is the open-loop diagram of an amplifier and servo motor and load.

(a) Write the transfer function C/R in the frequency response form.
(b) Plot the Bode diagram.
(c) Calculate and plot the phase angle for $\omega = $ 2, 6, 8, 12, 20 and 40.
(d) What are the breakpoints?
(e) What is the gain crossover frequency? the phase crossover frequency?
(f) What is the phase margin?
(g) What gain will this system have for a ω of 20? Check by calculation.
(h) As the gain of this system is reduced, it becomes less and less unstable. At what value of gain will it become or start to become stable?

12. A speed regulator with unity feedback has the following open-loop transfer function

$$\frac{S}{E} = \frac{K}{(1 + 0.04s)(1 + 0.0125s)}$$

With the use of a Bode diagram find the value of gain K that will give a phase margin of 40°.

Servo trainers

11.1. GENERAL

Most servo training kits are built in what is called *modular* or individual pieces or parts that may easily be connected together, both mechanically and electrically. They are primarily intended for experimental work in a laboratory giving a general qualitative grasp of closed-loop techniques as well as some more precise theoretical and analytical techniques.

This chapter examines one such trainer; it is built by Feedback, Inc., Berkeley Heights, N.J., especially for those students or readers who are just starting their study of the servo control field. Figures 11-21 through 11-24 show the different units of their modular dc and hybrid ac servo. The descriptions that follow, *i.e.*, the theory of unit operation of the Feedback equipment could, without too much difficulty, be adapted to cover the trainers built by other manufacturers. Figures 11-25 and 11-26 show the parts that make up the trainer built by Digiac Corp., Smithtown, N.Y. Figures 11-27 through 11-29 show the parts that comprise the trainer built by Electro-craft Corp., Hopkins, Minn.

11.2. THEORY COVERAGE

This section is mostly qualitative and covers the following:

1. Measurement of motor characteristics—field and armature control; transient response; Tach generator calibration

2. Properties of an operational amplifier; Speed control—forward and reverse; Effect of forward gain
3. Motor speed control behavior; Determining deadband; The error channel and closing the loop
4. Reduction of overshoot and settling time—velocity feedback; Effect of inertia; Stabilization; Field control
5. Synchro link; Demodulator action; Closed loop—synchro error link
6. Simulated relay unit; Relay system—open loop; Relay system—closed loop

11.3. MOTOR CHARACTERISTICS AND OPERATION

In any electrical-position or speed-control system, an electric motor is used along with its power supply and amplifier stage to control the power input in response to a lower level control signal. The motor should be reversible.

Figure 11-1(a) shows the armature connections, and figure 11-1(b) shows the field connections. In either circuit, a positive voltage at V_1 will forward bias the NPN transistor and will cause rotation in one direction. If this positive voltage is applied to terminal No. 2 on the servo amplifier instead of to terminal No. 1, the motor will reverse direction of rotation. Each connection has different characteristics, and each has certain advantages and disadvantages.

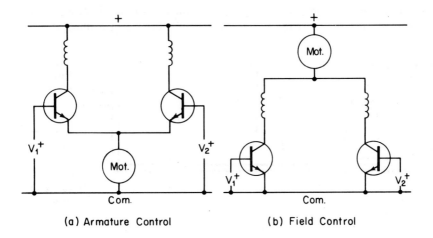

(a) Armature Control   (b) Field Control

FIG. 11-1. Basic Servo Motor Circuitry

In the connection in figure 11-1(a), the armature back emf appears between the emitter and ground, and thus the control voltage V_1 or V_2 must be increased in order to increase the motor speed. If the motor is loaded, the speed decreases and the current rises to provide the torque that is needed to keep the load moving with V_1 or V_2 being kept constant. A certain minimum motor voltage is required to start rotation.

In the connection in figure 11-1(b), the transistor current is determined largely by the input signal. Therefore, when the minimum voltage is reached and there is no load, the motor speed increases greatly with a small increase in input. Conversely, if the motor is loaded, then the speed will drop very rapidly. This makes the motor more difficult to control.

11.4. TRANSIENT RESPONSE

The first part of the first experiment, (see figure 11-2 for connections), will be concerned with the steady-state performance of the motor after a command signal has caused the motor to respond and *then* to settle down. Under ideal conditions, a motor, regardless of the type, should respond instantly to a command signal, and bring the system into correspondence. However, in any practical motor, there is always a time lag between the application of a command signal and the motor response. This lag exists because a torque must be generated to accelerate the armature and connected load, and this takes time; thus, the speed rises along an exponential curve (see figure 8-4, page 117). This exponential rise is exactly the same as the voltage rise across a capacitor in an RC circuit when the circuit is subjected to a step-voltage command. The time constant, τ_M, for the motor curve is determined by the parameters of mechanical friction, inertia, armature resistance, and back emf. Figure 11-3 illustrates this,

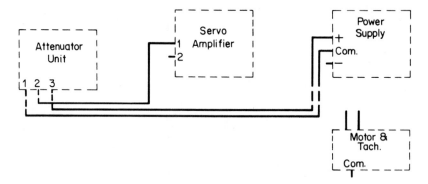

FIG. 11-2. Connections for Testing a Servo Motor

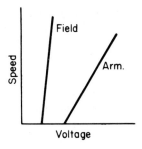
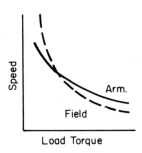

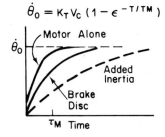

$$\dot{\theta}_0 = K_T V_C (1 - \epsilon^{-T/T_M})$$

$\dot{\theta}_0 = $ Velocity

$V_C = $ Volts

$K_T = $ Speed/Volts Applied

$\tau_M = $ Motor Time Constant

FIG. 11-3. Motor Characteristics for the Basic Methods of Control

and it also shows the difference in response when additional inertia is added to the motor shaft. Adding load will give the same response.

11.5. SPEED CONTROL

Some of the general characteristics of a closed-loop system may be investigated by or through the use of a simple speed-control system. In order to control speed, a signal that is proportional to that speed must be generated, and this may be done through the use of a tachometer-generator. The tachometer-generator is driven by the motor, directly or through gearing, and thus generates a voltage which is fed back to the comparator or summing junction. Here the voltage is compared with the reference voltage, and the difference between the two is the error signal which drives the motor to its preset speed level. If the gain of the forward path (open-loop gain) is large, then only a small error signal is required to operate the motor. As the forward gain is reduced, the error signal must increase in a still greater proportion to drive the motor. With gain very high, the motor is essentially controlled by the reference voltage. This may be proved in the following manner:

$$\dot{\theta}_0 = Ke \quad \dot{\theta}_0 = velocity \quad K = gain \quad e = error \quad (11\text{-}1)$$

$$e = V_c - K_G\dot{\theta}_0 \quad (11\text{-}2)$$

$K_G\dot{\theta}_0$ = tachometer voltage combining equations 11-1 and 11-2
$\dot{\theta}_0 = K(V_c - K_G\dot{\theta}_0) = KV_c - KK_G\dot{\theta}_0$ and dividing by $\dot{\theta}_0$

$$1 = \frac{KV_c}{\dot{\theta}_0} - KK_G \quad and \quad \frac{KV_c}{\dot{\theta}_0} = 1 + KK_G$$

$$\dot{\theta}_0 = \frac{KV_c}{1 + KK_G} \quad (11\text{-}3) \qquad If \ K \ is \ large, \ then \quad \dot{\theta}_0 = \frac{V_c}{KG}$$

If $K_G \cong$ constant then $\dot{\theta}_0 \cong V_c$
Also it can be shown that the error falls as the forward gain is increased.

$$e = V_c - KK_Ge \text{ and dividing by e}$$

$$1 = \frac{V_c}{e} - KK_G \quad and \quad \frac{V_c}{e} = 1 + KK_G$$

$$e = \frac{V_c}{1 + KK_G} \quad (11\text{-}4)$$

11.6.   THE OPERATIONAL AMPLIFIER

To investigate the response of the motor to a step-position command during the transient state, an operational amplifier will be used. This operational amplifier will compare signals and will also provide a high gain that can be varied. Figure 11-4 shows the three different operational amplifier circuits that can be used and their resultant voltage outputs. Figure 11-4(a) is a summing circuit, figure 11-4(b) introduces a scaling factor, and figure 11-4(c) gives an output that is comparable to that of an ideal motor. When the circuit of 11-4(b) is used with a feedback signal plugged into the external feedback sockets, full amplifier gain is not available. Under any condition, the *maximum amplifier output is about* 12V. When $R_1 = R_2$ (control switch to the left), the output is the sum of the input voltages but with a minus sign. If $R_1 \neq R_2$, then a scaling factor is introduced, and, when $R_1 = R_2$ and a capacitor is in parallel

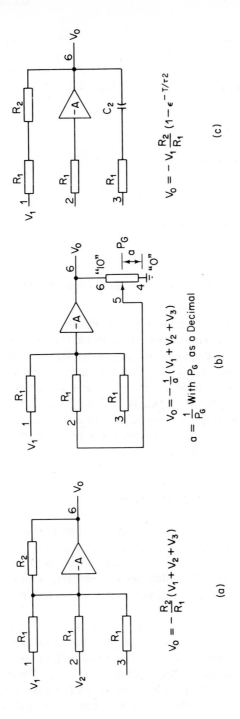

FIG. 11-4. Operational Amplifier Circuits Used for Comparing Signals

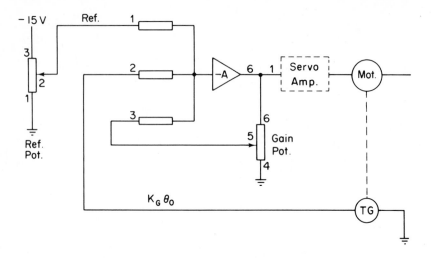

FIG. 11-5. Connections for a Speed Control System

with the feedback resistor (control switch in the middle), the output voltage has the form shown in figure 11-3. When the control switch is at the right, provision is made to connect an external feedback signal around the amplifier across terminals 4 and 5. If it is necessary to zero the operational amplifier, it may be done by measuring the output voltage at terminal 6 with no inputs at terminals 1, 2, or 3 and with the control switch at the left. The output should be zero, thus showing that the $\pm 15V$ supplies balance internally. If the output is not zero, then adjust the zero adjustment knob until the output is zero.

11.7. REVERSIBLE SPEED CONTROL

When a servo system requires control in either direction of rotation, it is necessary to reverse the reference voltage; this means that the final servo amplifier must have two input sockets. The operational amplifier does not have such reversible ability, so a preamplifier unit is introduced between the attenuator unit (reference potentiometer) and the servo amplifier.

The preamplifier has two output sockets and two input sockets as shown in figure 11-6. A positive voltage applied to either input gives a positive output at one output socket; a negative voltage applied to either input gives a positive output at the other output socket. These two output sockets then provide the drive for both inputs on the servo amplifier, and the motor will respond in either direction. The overall gain of the pre-

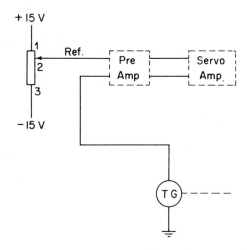

FIG. 11-6. Connections for Reversible Speed Control

amplifier is about 25, and maximum output is about 12V. Figure 11-7 shows the better speed control and gain associated with the preamplifier.

If it is necessary to zero the preamplifier, it may be done by measuring the output at terminals No. 3 and No. 4 when there is no input to terminals No. 1 and No. 2. These output voltages should be approximately 1.0 to 1.2V, thus showing that the ± 15V supplies balance internally. If not, then adjust the zero adjustment knob until the voltages balance. If they still will not balance, then the "preset" zero can be adjusted.

In the simple speed-control system that is shown in figure 11-5, whenever a step-position change of voltage is made, the response is such that the motor speed comes up to the final value without overshooting, as

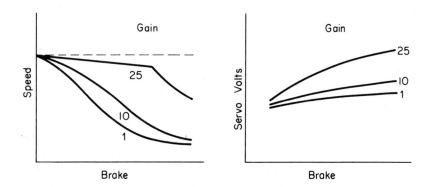

FIG. 11-7. Speed Control Characteristics for Different Values of Gain

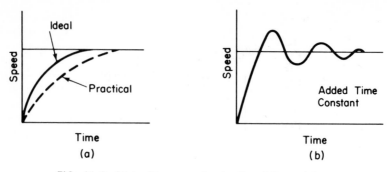

FIG. 11-8. Motor Responses for the Speed Control System

is illustrated in figure 11-8(a). As long as the signals in the system do not exceed the operating range of each unit, *i.e.*, saturation of an amplifier, the response follows an exponential curve. If the maximum signal ranges are exceeded, then response will be slower.

If an additional time constant should take place in the forward path, then the response may be such that overshooting takes place. The reason for this is that the extra time delay prevents the increased signal to the servo amplifier from being reduced as quickly as the error is reduced; thus, the motor may oscillate before settling down. This is illustrated in figure 11-8(b). To observe the effect of an additional time delay on motor performance, the RC network in the operational amplifier should be inserted in the forward path.

In the speed-control system that is shown in figure 11-9, the output of the tachometer-generator is fed into the operational amplifier, rather than the preamplifier, so that the error signal can be displayed. The error is the difference between the command voltage and the tachometer voltage. When the error is zero, the system is running at some definite speed and is termed a *velocity control system*.

Figure 11-10 shows the display of the velocity signal or tachometer output and the error signal for different values of gain. It clearly shows that when gain is high, deadband is small, and, when gain is low, deadband is large. It also shows that high gain gives very good speed response with an error of peak value only at the instant of motor reversal. However, when gain is reduced, the response is still good, but the final speed of the motor is reduced and there is a larger error.

When an additional time delay or a larger load is added, the system becomes more and more oscillatory. If both occur, then the response is slowed down greatly and the error change is also slowed down. This may be caused by the fact that the power supply is overloaded, and it just cannot supply the necessary power.

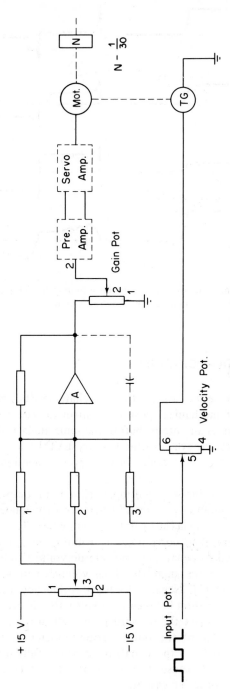

FIG. 11-9. A Complete Velocity Control System

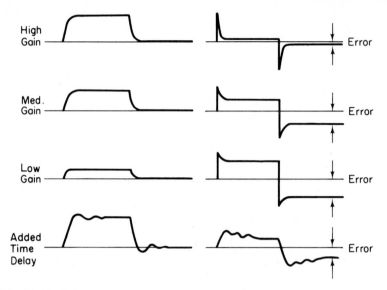

FIG. 11-10. A Comparison of Velocity and Error Signals for Different Values of Gain
in a Velocity Control System

11.8.   THE ERROR CHANNEL

Another scheme for investigating the characteristics of a closed-loop
system is that of mechanical position control (a true servomechanism)
where a motor drives an output shaft to the same angle as that of an input
shaft.   Potentiometers, synchros, and rotary LVDT's are excellent transducers to use in such a system.   In dc servos, potentiometers are used
most often.

A reference or input potentiometer and an output or feedback
potentiometer form an *error channel* when properly connected with their
slider voltages summed via the operational amplifier.   To properly connect
the potentiometers, their corresponding winding ends, (1, 2) and (2, 1),
must be connected to equal and opposite dc voltage supplies so that, if
the two shaft angles are equal, the slider voltages will be equal and will
cancel (see figure 11-11).   Negative feedback is thus obtained.   Any sudden
change in angular position between the two shafts will give an error signal
which, in turn, will drive the forward path.   When the loop is closed by
connecting the slider of the output potentiometer to the operational
amplifier, the polarities of the signals must be carefully observed because
the error signal should cause the servo motor to rotate in a direction to
reduce the error, not to increase it.

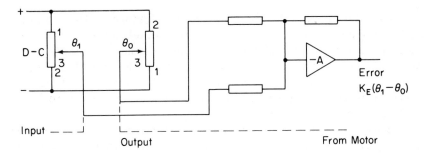

FIG. 11-11. Potentiometer Error Channel for a Position Control System

11.9. GENERAL PERFORMANCE

Two characteristics of a simple position servo that are of interest are the deadband and the transient response. The deadband is the minimum signal that is required by the system in order for it to respond. In the first experiment, the motor did not start until a minimum voltage was applied, this is the deadband, and it is inversely proportional to gain.

The transient response is studied in terms of overshoot and settling time. Overshoot takes place because of system response to an input change. If a step-position command occurs, an error signal is set up which will drive the motor until it passes through the alignment point. At this point, the motor has velocity and will drive on through the point; thus, the error signal reverses, and the motor slows down, stops, reverses, and tries to drive to realignment in the reverse direction. But again, overshooting may result until the system finally settles down. For low values of gain, little overshooting takes place, but, as gain is increased, the overshooting and the settling time both increase as is shown in figure 11-12.

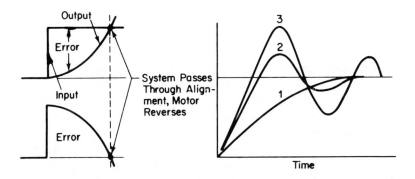

FIG. 11-12. Transient Motor Conditions

It can now be seen that, if gain is low, the deadband is large and the system responds slowly; as gain is increased, deadband is reduced and oscillations now occur, but system response is quicker. Ideally, gain should be high, deadband low, and response time low with little or no overshoot. One way to achieve this is to add additional load via the magnetic brake, but this means that additional power is required from the motor, which may not be available.

A second way to achieve this is to use a signal that is proportional to motor speed or velocity, i.e., a signal from the tachometer-generator. If the drive power could be reversed before the system reaches the alignment point, then the motor would already be slowing up as this point is reached, and the overshoot would be greatly reduced. This is shown in figure 11-13(a). The signal from the tachometer-generator is a direct measure of the output shaft speed which may be increasing as the system comes into alignment. If this signal is fed back into the summation point and is negative when it is added to the error, then the sum of the signals becomes zero and may even reverse before the system reaches alignment. Therefore, the motor drive reverses before alignment, and the system slows down without the excessive overshoot. The major disadvantage is that the speed of response decreases as velocity feedback is increased. See figures 11-13(b) and 11-13(c). Figure 11-13(b) is the general block diagram and shows that the tachometer-generator is connected in a second or inner loop. Polarities must be carefully observed around both the outer and inner loops in order to ensure that the system responds correctly.

A third way is to increase the effective inertia of the motor by adding more inertia to the motor shaft by using an inertia disc. If this inertia disc is placed on a shaft that is geared to the motor, then its effect will be quite a bit different. This is because of the gear reduction ratio, N. Inertia on a low speed shaft would be reduced by $1/N^2$, or by about $1/900$ at the armature for this servo.

11.10.   INSTABILITY AND STABILIZATION

In the experimental work done so far, any transients that have occurred have died away, thus giving a stable system. However, in many practical systems, the oscillations may continue, rather than decrease, and the system becomes unstable. This is particularly true when there is a lot of inertia but little or no friction.

Any additional time delays in the forward path that have been introduced for whatever reason will also lead to instability. Filters that are used to eliminate noise or other spurious signals contribute to the problem of stabilizing a system.

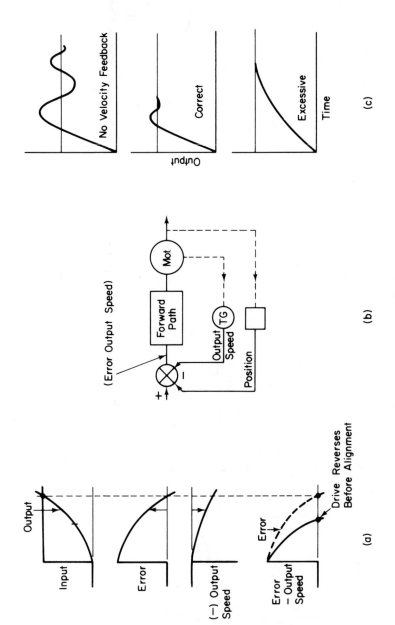

FIG. 11-13. Effect of Tach Generator (Velocity) Feedback

181

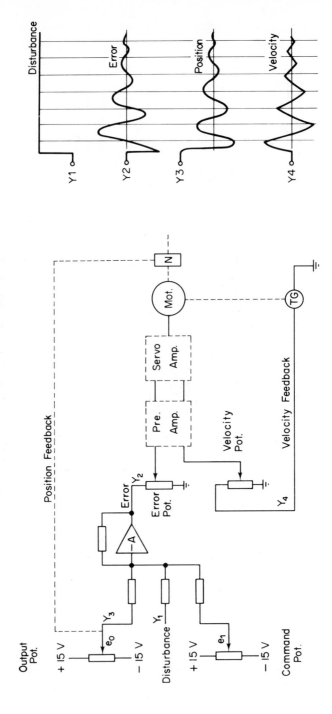

FIG. 11-14. A Complete Mechanical Position Control System with Signal Traces

Increasing the sensitivity of a system (reducing deadband) by using field control, rather than armature control, may also lead to instability, unless other corrections are taken. The speed of an unloaded motor with field control increases to a very high value with low input (see figure 11-3). Velocity feedback shifts the characteristic to a level that is closer to that of an armature-controlled motor.

Figure 11-14 shows the complete mechanical position control system. The oscilloscope traces show the effect an outside disturbance has on the desired position with resulting error and finally the velocity stabilization.

11.11. AC CONTROL SYSTEMS

All the control systems studied on the previous pages have used a dc error channel, a dc servo motor with potentiometers being used as the error detectors. If one desires that synchros be used as error detectors, then the ac error signal must be demodulated to provide a dc signal to drive the servo motor. There is no requirement for an operational amplifier because the difference between input and output signals is actually produced in the synchro CT. A hybrid system using synchros and a demodulator is shown in figures 11-15 and 11-16.

11.12. RELAY-CONTROLLED SYSTEMS

There are servo systems in which the motor is controlled by a relay rather than by an amplifier. Figure 11-17 shows the general schematic diagram of such a system. The error signal will energize the relay coil which in turn will switch power to the motor. The relay may be *three position, i.e.,* one position drives the motor in a forward direction, a second

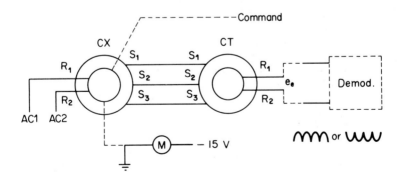

FIG. 11-15. Synchro Transducers

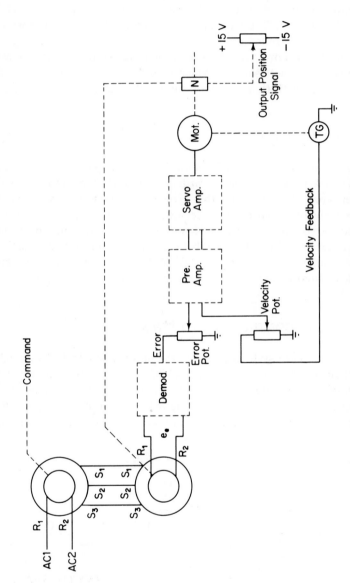

FIG. 11-16. A Complete Mechanical Position Control System with Synchro Transducers

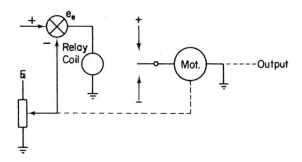

FIG. 11-17. Basic Relay Connections

position drives the motor in the reverse direction, and a third position results when the relay is deenergized and the motor is stopped. The relay might be *two position* which means that power is always applied to the motor, either in one direction or the other.

In reality, the relay is an amplifier in which a small amount of coil power controls contacts, which in turn control a larger amount of power that is applied to the motor. However, the power that is applied to the motor is not of a continuous adjustment as it would be with an amplifier; therefore, the performance of the relay system is not as precise as that of a power amplifier.

The characteristics of relays may be represented by plotting output against input. A two-position relay that controls power in either direction and changes over when the coil signal (error) changes sign has the characteristics shown in figure 11-18(a); it is an "ideal" one. Hysteresis, which most two-position relays have, is shown in figure 11-18(b); the relay cannot operate there until a positive or negative signal voltage of a

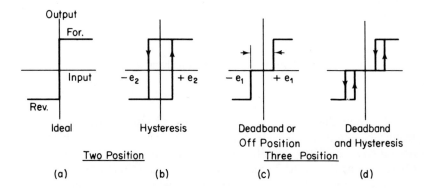

FIG. 11-18. Characteristics of a Two-position and a Three-position Relay

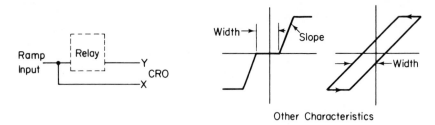

FIG. 11-19. Effect of Adjustable Slope and Deadband

minimum value is present. A three-position relay with an "off" position gives the deadband characteristic that is shown in figure 11-18(c); here, an input of plus or minus e is required to operate the relay. Figure 11-18(d) shows the characteristic of a three-position relay that has both deadband and hysteresis on the switching level.

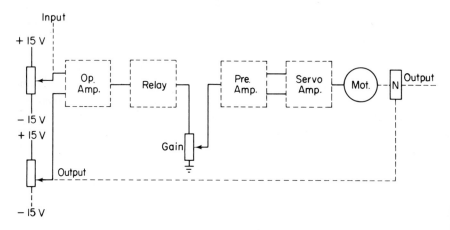

FIG. 11-20. A Relay Controlling a Mechanical Position Servo

The unit that is used to simulate these characteristics does so electronically, and it also provides some additional characteristics which relays do not have, namely (1) limiting with adjustable slope and deadband, and (2) adjustable backlash. Because it is a small unit, it does not have enough power to operate the motor directly; therefore, the output feeds the normal preamplifier and power amplifier. Figures 11-19 and 11-20 show the experimental connections.

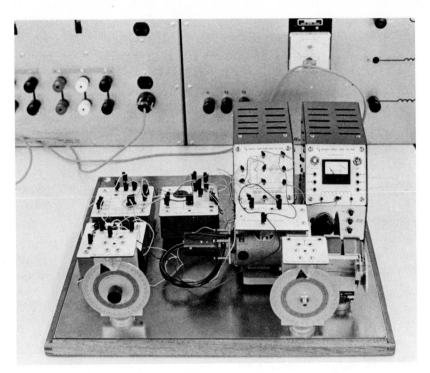

FIG. 11-21. DC Servo Trainer (Courtesy of Feedback, Inc., Berkeley Heights, N.J.)

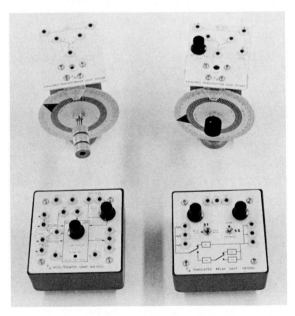

FIG. 11-22. Miscellaneous Servo Devices, Synchros,
etc. (Courtesy of Feedback, Inc., Berkeley Heights, N.J.)

FIG. 11-23. Miscellaneous Servo Devices, Modulator/Demodulator, etc.
(Courtesy of Feedback, Inc., Berkeley Heights, N.J.)

FIG. 11-24. AC Servo Trainer with Logic Bits and Shaft Encoder (Courtesy
of Feedback, Inc., Berkeley Heights, N.J.)

11.13.   DIGIAC CORPORATION SERVO
TRAINER

The philosophy of this company in the design and production of its Servomechanisms trainer is that the experience that is gained in the laboratory is one of the most important aspects in preparing a student for work in the field of automatic control of machinery.

The laboratory equipment shown in figures 11-25 and 11-26 uses dc,

FIG. 11-25. Servomechanisms Trainer (Courtesy of Digiac Corp., Smithtown, N.Y.)

rather than ac, because the dc servomotor and its associated devices demonstrate in a much clearer fashion the basic principles of feedback control. The approach is essentially practical with very little dependence on higher mathematics, *i.e.*, the calculus. The experimental procedures that can be followed with this equipment lead from the very simple to the more complex. However, the equipment has a flexibility that allows a student to do more advanced experiments if he so desires.

FIG. 11-26. Servo Motor and Transducer (Courtesy of Digiac Corp., Smithtown, N.Y.)

11.14.   ELECTRO-CRAFT CORPORATION SERVO TRAINER

The philosophy of this company in the design and production of its Servo Trainer or Control Systems Laboratory equipment is that the experience that is gained in the laboratory is one of the most important aspects in preparing a student for work in the servo or automatic control field.

The laboratory equipment (Motomatic Control System) is dc in nature because the dc servomotor and controller principle has proved to be far superior to the traditional ac motor approach for many industrial applications. All the principles of feedback control can be demonstrated in a much more lucid fashion by using dc rather than ac servo devices. The equipment has been designed in such a manner, *i.e.*, flexibility, that many different experiments may be performed other than those that are considered standard. The following figures 11-27 through 11-29 illustrate very graphically what this equipment is.

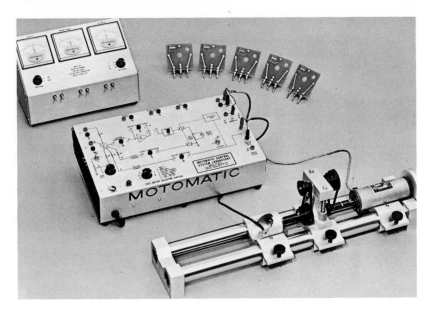

FIG. 11-27. Motomatic Servo Trainer (Courtesy of Electro Craft Corp., Hopkins, Minn.)

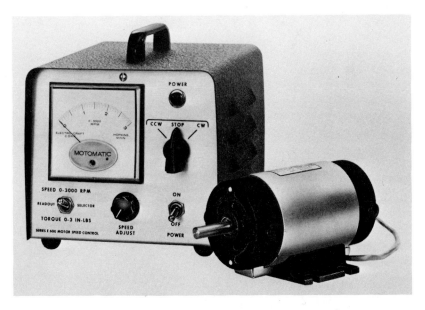

FIG. 11-28. Servo Motor and Speed Control Unit (Courtesy of Electro Craft Corp., Hopkins, Minn.)

FIG. 11-29. Motomatic Servo Experimenter (Courtesy of Electro
Craft Corp., Hopkins, Minn.)

TWELVE

Other electro-mechanical devices

SHAFT ENCODERS

12.1. INTRODUCTION

When one desires to change an analog signal such as speed, voltage or position to a digital signal to obtain greater accuracy, or when it is desired to operate with very small error signals, it is best to use a digital servomechanism. In order to deal with both signals, *i.e.*, to go from analog to digital, an A to D converter is needed. This conversion may be accomplished by a shaft encoder in which the shaft position is an analog measurement, and it may represent the direction of a radar screen, the position of the rudder of an aircraft or any number of different automatic control applications.

An encoder is an electromechanical device that can be fastened to a rotating shaft to produce a series of pulses to indicate shaft position. As it has a shaft, housing, and electrical outputs, it looks somewhat like a motor. In reality, it is simply a rotating switch with a number of poles and positions that vary depending on the type of encoder.

Encoding, which means assigning digital values to mechanical motion, takes place when the shaft of the encoder is coupled, either through gears or a flexible coupling, to the output shaft of the system under test or study. It thus produces coded combinations of outputs from analog inputs, namely, analog to digital conversion. Two basic types of encoders are (1) the *incremental* or *pulse* type, and (2) the *absolute* type. These two types look somewhat alike, but they differ quite a bit in their method of operation.

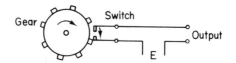

FIG. 12-1. A Simple Gear-type Mechanical Encoder

12.2. INCREMENTAL ENCODER

The basic operation of an incremental encoder is that, as its shaft is turned, a stream of pulses is generated on a pair of output wires. Each pulse represents some fraction of a revolution of the shaft. A mechanical analogy would be a gear with a small number of teeth rotating so that the teeth close a snap-action, spring-return microswitch. Each time a tooth touches the switch and closes the circuit, an output voltage can be measured (see figure 12-1).

One complete revolution of the gear would produce eight pulses, each pulse representing 45°. At each tooth, the pulse is the same as the one before it; therefore, the angle is determined by storing and counting the pulses. Thus, the count at any time is the number of angular increments through which the shaft has been rotated.

The most common way to generate a pulse is through the use of optics. Here, a disc that has been constructed with alternating transparent- and opaque-rimmed sections is rotated between a light source and a photo-detector. The opaque or dark segments of the disc serve to interrupt the light source, and thus a pulse is created. Figure 12-2 shows such a disc. In this example, however, the electronics cannot "know" the direction of shaft rotation because either direction gives the same pulse trains. An encoder built in this manner is called a *unidirectional incremental encoder*. To become bidirectional, more complex circuitry is required. Also, if power fails or is turned off, the count is lost. Another disadvantage is that extraneous electrical noise or pickup might very well be counted as a pulse and thus produce a wrong count.

Advantages really depend on the application. For example, (1) if rate or velocity is being measured, (2) if counting of pieces or parts is required, (3) if a zero reset regardless of shaft position is required, (4) if the shaft always rotates in one direction, or (5) if loss of power or noise is not a problem, then an incremental encoder will be the best to use.

12.3. ABSOLUTE ENCODER

The basic operation of an *absolute encoder* is that it consists of a coded disc and brushes that sense the code pattern. There are usually

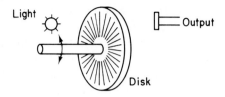

FIG. 12-2. A Simple Optical Disc Encoder

several concentric tracks on a disc with each track being composed of alternately conducting and nonconducting segments. The innermost track will have fairly long segments but only a few of them, while the track at the outside of the disc will have a large number of smaller segments. Each track will thus differ in segment length and number as the track diameter changes. Depending on the code being used, each of the different tracks may represent distinct digits or the output wires which make up a digit. Figure 12-3 shows an elementary type. These tracks normally mean that the absolute encoder has quite a few more leads than the incremental type. If slip rings or long leads are required to bring the outputs out, then there will be an increased cost. Other disadvantages are that rate or velocity data cannot be measured easily, and, when zeroing is required, it cannot be done easily, unless it operates into a computer.

Advantages are that they are insensitive to noise or pickup, a count cannot be lost because of power failure, and digital outputs will follow changes in shaft rotation without any problem.

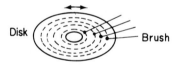

FIG. 12-3. A Simple Coded Disc Encoder

12.4. BASIC TECHNIQUES

As was stated in the beginning, an encoder is like a rotating switch with many poles and positions. Now there are basically two ways of doing this switching; they are referred to as (1) *contacting*, and (2) *noncontacting*. In the contacting style, a wire brush moves along a coded disc or commutator, thus the name *brush type encoder*. In the noncontacting style, a circuit parameter such as voltage, current, or resistance changes quite abruptly in response to the switching of a light beam, a magnetic field or capacitive coupling. The most common noncontacting method is through the use of optics (light beams).

As to which one is best to use, it is again a toss up, and it depends on the application. Thus, pick an optical or incremental encoder when (1) more than 10,000 counts/turn accuracy is required, (2) very, very low starting torques of less than 0.1 oz-in are required, and (3) high speeds especially above 5000 rpm and of continuous nature are required. A brush type or absolute encoder would be picked for applications when (1) environmental problems such as dripping liquid, acidic atmospheres, and heavy shocks are prevalent, (2) high wattage of 50W or more is needed to the load, and (3) other applications where long life and reliability are demanded.

12.5. LOGIC AND CODES

In any shaft encoder, it is quite difficult to synchronize positionally each brush/track or optic circuit combination with all the others. To prevent signals that are out of sequence from reaching the output, logic circuits are used to ensure that all brushes and tracks or optics are precisely in alignment. Logic circuits help to eliminate electrical noise generated by the brushes or optics, and they also help to provide longer life for the encoder.

When encoders were first used, industry was using counting systems based on the powers of ten; however, as computer technology became more advanced, a different counting system was used. A relay has an on-off characteristic the same as a transistor so that a counting system could be used. Thus, the number 3150 would be represented as $1 \times 2^{11} + 1 \times 2^{10} + 1 \times 2^6 + 1 \times 2^3 + 1 \times 2^2 + 1 \times 2^1$; all other coefficients of two are zero. The number is written as 110001001110 and would be instrumented as a 12-wire line. The wires connecting or representing the "1's" would have voltage on them relative to a common point, while the "0's" are at zero potential (see figure 12-4).

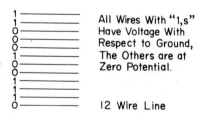

All Wires With "1,s" Have Voltage With Respect to Ground, The Others are at Zero Potential.

12 Wire Line

FIG. 12-4. A 12-wire line in a Simple Counting System

TABLE 12-1
A Comparison of Three Counting Codes

Decimal	Binary	Gray
0	0	000
1	1	001
2	10	011
3	11	010
4	100	110
5	101	111
6	110	101
7	111	100

If one desires to combine both the decimal and the binary system, then the Binary-Coded Decimal (BCD) system in which four binary rows are used for each digit used. The number 3150 is now represented as:

$$2^3 \quad 2^2 \quad 2^1 \quad 2^0$$

0011   0001   0101   0 0 0 0

3   1   5   0

Shaft encoders that use brushes create problems in that, if one of the brushes accidently touches an adjacent row because of mechanical problems, then large errors in the count could result. To prevent this, the Gray code is used so that any chance of error is eliminated; however, additional brushes and more electronic circuits are required. To go from binary to the Gray code is a simple matter. The number written in binary is converted by changing any digit immediately preceded by a "1" to its opposite state. The number 3150, for example, would change from 110001001110 to 101001101001. Table 12-1 shows the relationship between decimal, binary and Gray code numbers.

If we look at the binary code, we can see why the Gray code is more advantageous to use. When the binary code advances from 3 to 4 (011 to 100), all three bits must change state from "0" to "1" or from "1" to "0." However, it is almost impossible to design mechanical switches that will all change state at exactly the same time. Therefore, if some switches open or close sooner or later than others, the transition from 011 to 100 may appear to go through several states such as 011→111→101→100. The false states may only last for a very short period of time, but a digital computer might respond to them, and erroneous outputs could result. Note that as the Gray code is advanced from number to number, only one bit of the code changes state.

Figure 12-5 shows a binary-coded disc, and figure 12-6 shows a Gray-coded disc. In these discs, the black sections may represent con-

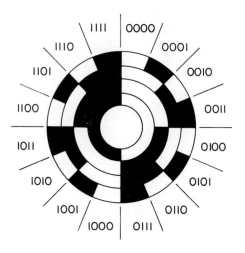

FIG. 12-5. Binary Code Disc

ducting surfaces so that brushes riding on the disc at each of the concentric rings can give an output whenever they make contact with a conducting surface, or they may represent opaque sections on a transparent disc so that light is blocked for the proper digits.

The application in which the encoder is used really determines which code is the best to use. Industrial applications have used the decimal code for years, especially for outputs that are displayed, so they probably will

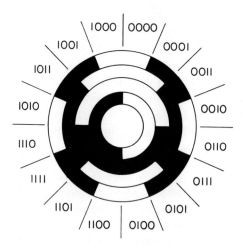

FIG. 12-6. Gray Code Disc

continue to use this code. If one desires to have the readout used with a computer, then the BCD might be best. Binary code is the heart of computer language, yet the Gray code is capable of a greater number of bits in relationship to the pulses generated.

STEPPER MOTORS

12.6. GENERAL

A stepper motor is an electromagnetic device that converts digital pulse inputs into analog output shaft movements with these steps being equal to the number of input pulses. They can thus be used for remote-positioning control systems in a wide variety of industrial drives such as printers, tape drives, capstan drives, machine tool and numerical control drives, and process control drives. They also can be used for variable speed drives such as curve tracers, and feed drives in chart recorders.

Advantages of the stepper motor are (1) that being a digital device, it interfaces readily with a computer and other digital components, (2) it has long life and fast response, and (3) it has good open-loop stability when properly matched to the system's requirements. This means that other transducers such as a tachometer-generator, synchros, and potentiometers can be eliminated.

12.7. TYPES

Five basic types of stepper motors are in general use; they are (1) variable-reluctance type, (2) solenoid-ratchet type, (3) permanent magnet type, (4) synchronous type—phase controlled, and (5) harmonic-drive type. The two most widely used types are the variable reluctance and the permanent magnet. Variable-reluctance types usually provide higher torques, larger stepping rates, and smaller stepping angles than do the permanent magnet types, although the newer permanent magnets are about the same in performance. The permanent magnet type, however, does have two other important advantages, and these advantages are (1) better damping, and (2) small overshoot.

The permanent magnet type usually consists of a cylindrical permanent magnet rotor rotating within a laminated, slotted stator which contains the windings. The rotor is magnetized along a diameter and may have one or more pairs of poles. The stator winding may be two, three, four, six or eight phases. In operation, the rotor lines up with the stator

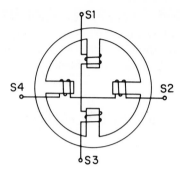

FIG. 12-7. Simplified Diagram of a 2-pole Stator

magnetic field produced by applying a dc voltage to the stator coils. When the polarity of the dc voltage is switched in a definite order, the stator field will rotate in either clockwise or counterclockwise steps.

12.8.   SWITCHING MODES—
PERMANENT MAGNET TYPE

For simplicity in the following discussion, the windings will be considered to be wound on salient poles. Figure 12-7 shows such an arrangement for a two-pole stepper motor (two poles in each of the two phases).

With the positive of the supply connected to S1 and the negative connected to S3, a magnetic field is produced by the stator. The rotor lines up with this stator field as is shown in figure 12-8(a) (solid shading indicates a north pole). If the positive is now switched from S1 to S2 and the negative from S3 to S4, then a magnetic field is produced as is shown in figure 12-8(b). The field has now rotated 90°. Subsequent polarity changes as are shown in figures 12-8(c) and 12-8(d) rotate the stator field, and thus the rotor, through 360° in 90° increments. It should be noted that each position is unique, and that no positional ambiguity exists.

The sequence of polarities to obtain 90° stepping as described above is given in table 12-2.

TABLE 12-2
Switching Mode "A" (90° Step Angle)

Step Position	S1	S2	S3	S4
1 Fig. 12-8(A)	+	0	−	0
2 Fig. 12-8(B)	0	+	0	−
3 Fig. 12-8(C)	−	0	+	0
4 Fig. 12-8(D)	0	−	0	+

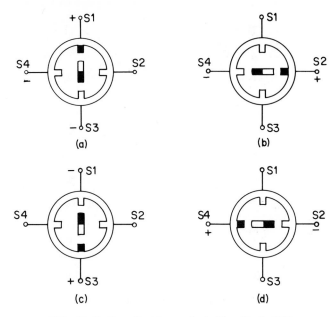

FIG. 12-8. Step Positions—Switching Mode "A"

Another method of obtaining a 90° stepping mode is to use the resultant of two fields as is shown in figure 12-9.

The sequence of polarities to obtain 90° stepping as shown in figure 12-9 is given in table 12-3.

Since with this method two windings are energized at the same time, the current and power input are 100% higher than with the previous method, but the torque is only 41% higher.

It is obvious from figures 12-8 and 12-9 that a proper combination of the two methods will result in a 45° stepping mode. The polarity sequence is given in table 12-4.

Switching the polarities as is shown in tables 12-2, 12-3 and 12-4 is readily accomplished with mechanical switching devices.   To do this

TABLE 12-3
Switching Mode "B" (90° Step Angle)

Step Position	S1	S2	S3	S4
1 Fig. 12-9(A)	+	+	−	−
2 Fig. 12-9(B)	−	+	+	−
3 Fig. 12-9(C)	−	−	+	+
4 Fig. 12-9(D)	+	−	−	+

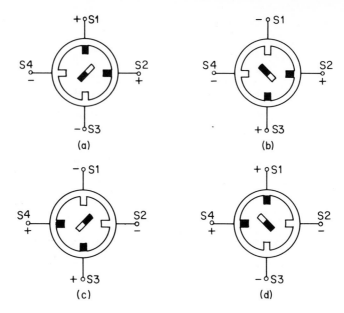

FIG. 12-9. Step Positions—Switching Mode "B"

electronically with solid-state components is rather complex because two polarities have to be switched.

In order to simplify the electronic driving circuit, stepper motors are usually made with a center-tap in each winding. They are then called four-phase stepper motors. A simplified diagram is shown in figure 12-10.

By connecting both center-taps to one terminal, *e.g.*, the positive, of the supply and switching the other terminal as is shown in tables 12-5 and 12-6, rotation of the stepper motor is the same as in figures 12-9 and 12-10.

By combining the switching modes of tables 12-5 and 12-6 in the proper sequence, 45° stepping is also obtained as is shown in table 12-7.

TABLE 12-4
Switching Mode "C" (45° Step Angle)

Step Position	S1	S2	S3	S4
1 Fig. 12-8(A)	+	0	−	0
2 Fig. 12-9(A)	+	+	−	−
3 Fig. 12-8(B)	0	+	0	−
4 Fig. 12-9(B)	−	+	+	−
5 Fig. 12-8(C)	−	0	+	0
6 Fig. 12-9(C)	−	−	+	+
7 Fig. 12-8(D)	0	−	0	+
8 Fig. 12-9(D)	+	−	−	+

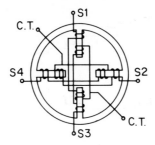

FIG. 12-10. Simplified Diagram of a 4-phase Stator

TABLE 12-5
Switching Mode "D" (90° Step Angle)

Step Position	S1	S2	S3	S4
1	0	0	—	0
2	0	0	0	—
3	—	0	0	0
4	0	—	0	0

TABLE 12-6
Switching Mode "E" (90° Step Angle)

Step Position	S1	S2	S3	S4
1	0	0	—	—
2	—	0	0	—
3	—	—	0	0
4	0	—	—	0

TABLE 12-7
Switching Mode "F" (45° Step Angle)

Step Position	S1	S2	S3	S4
1	0	0	—	0
2	0	0	—	—
3	0	0	0	—
4	—	0	0	—
5	—	0	0	0
6	—	—	0	0
7	0	—	0	0
8	0	—	—	0

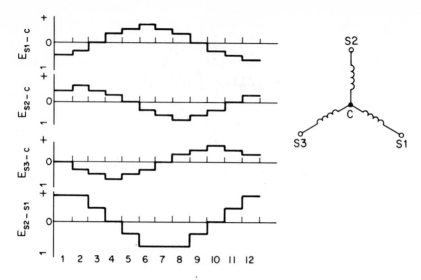

FIG. 12-11. Switching Waveforms for 30° Steps

12.9. A COMPARISON OF SWITCHING MODES

A comparison of the various switching modes is given in table 12-8. Mode "E" is used as the basis for comparison since it gives the highest torque for the simplest electronic driving circuit.

Four-phase stepper motors can of course be used as two-phase motors by leaving the center-taps disconnected.

Three-phase stepper motors operate in a similar manner to those types that have already been covered. The switching wave forms obtained from 30° stepping are shown in figure 12-11.

Two ways in which the switching of the dc driving voltage can be accomplished are through stepping transmitters (mechanical drives) and

TABLE 12-8
Comparison of Switching Modes

Switching Mode	Torque	Total Current and Power Input	Torque Per Unit of Power Input
A	70%	25%	280%
B	100%	50%	200%
C	85% Avg.	37% Avg.	230%
D	70%	50%	140%
E	100%	100%	100%
F	85% Avg.	85% Avg.	100%

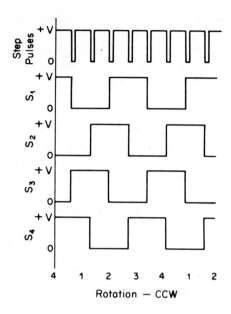

FIG. 12-12. Typical Logic Waveforms from Electronic Driver

all electronic drivers. The mechanical transmitter can be fitted with microswitches operated by an eccentric shaft and the correct gearing so that high resolution is obtained. If diodes are used for suppression, then correct power line polarity must be observed. Figure 12-11 shows the voltage waveforms developed across a three-phase stepper motor.

The electronic driver is an all-transistorized logic driver that accepts pulses on one or two lines (clockwise or counterclockwise) and processes these pulses via two flip-flops operated in a forced count sequence. The output of the flip-flops is then fed through buffer amplifiers to drive the stepper motor. Figure 12-12 shows some typical logic waveforms.

12.10. DEVELOPED TORQUE OF STEPPER MOTORS

STATIC CONDITIONS. At rest, in a particular step position, the rotor is lined up with the stator field, and no torque exists to move it to a different position. If the rotor is moved away from this lined-up position by external mechanical means, then a restoring torque will be developed.

It should be noted that at 90° displacement maximum torque is developed. This is called *holding torque* and is used as a figure of merit. The stepper motor cannot drive a load requiring a torque equal to the holding torque since this occurs only at 90° displacement. At other positions, the torque is lower. *Pull-out torque* (sometimes called *running torque*) is the proper indication of the loading capacity of the motor. The pull-out torque varies with the *switching rate*, and it is limited by the inherent damping in the motor. Load inertia has little or no effect on pull-out torque.

DYNAMIC CONDITIONS. If instead of moving the rotor as described under "Static Conditions," the polarities are changed so that the stator field moves to the next step position, then the same relative condition occurs. In the case of a 90° stepper motor, maximum torque is developed at the moment of switching. Because of this torque, the rotor moves, and, without any load connected to it, it will line up with the stator field at the new step position.

However, if a load is connected to the rotor, then the load torque tends to hold the rotor at a certain displacement from the stator field position. The combined inertia of the load and rotor has an oscillatory effect. Damping is present in the form of friction, eddy currents and hysteresis.

In between the regions of operation mentioned above, there is a range of switching rates where the stepper motor behaves erratically. Stepping still occurs but with irregular step angles. The pull-out torque varies considerably, and it is at certain switching rates lower than at higher rates. By careful selection of load inertia and additional damping, this effect can be minimized.

If the switching rate is increased and operation becomes stable as mentioned above, there comes a point, with further increase in switching rate, where the motor cannot accelerate the load plus motor inertia from standstill to synchronous speed. Here, the *pull-in rate*, which is the top of the *response range*, is reached. This means that between the zero switching rate and the pull-in rate the motor can start, stop and reverse on command. A small nebulous range around the pull-in rate exists wherein the stepper motor can bring the load to synchronism, but not without losing some steps. The pull-in rate varies with the total inertia. In the response range, the stepper motor can be successfully used as an open-loop positioning device with no-load step position errors of about 1°. A load that is applied to the stepper motor will increase the line-up inaccuracy by an amount determined by the torque gradient.

If the switching rate is increased still further while the motor is running, the *slew range* is reached. In this range, the motor cannot start, stop or reverse on command, but it develops enough torque to overcome the load torque. This is a useful range, provided means can be devised to bring the motor to these speeds out of the response range.

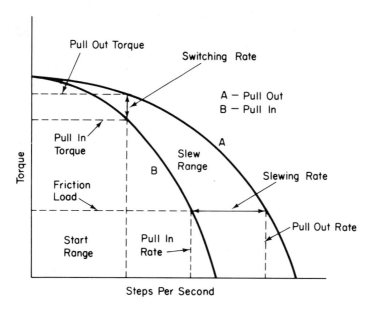

FIG. 12-13. Stepper Motor Characteristics

The switching rate can be increased until the *pull-out range* is reached, at which point the inherent damping decreases the available torque to below the level of the load torque. This is at the top of the slew range.

A summary of the performance characteristics explained above is given in figure 12-13.

12.11. USE IN CONTROL SYSTEMS

There are two distinctly different ways of using stepper motors in control systems. One is the open-loop system, and the other is the positional feedback or closed-loop system. Both have advantages over conventional servo systems. Figures 12-14 through 12-16 show some block diagram examples of stepper motor uses in these two modes.

The open-loop stepper motor system is quite unique, and it has no exact equivalent in the conventional servo system. The stepper motor is a digital device whose output in shaft angular displacement is completely determined by the number of input pulses. The motor can thus position an object accurately on an input command in the form of a number of pulses. However, the motor must be used in its response range, *i.e.*, where it can start, stop and reverse on command. An important advantage of the open-loop system is that any error is noncumulative. The elimination of

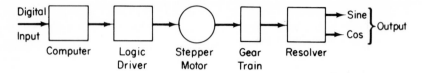

FIG. 12-14. Digital-to-analog-Conversion

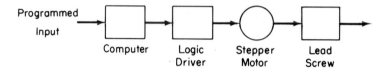

FIG. 12-15. Machine Tool Positioner

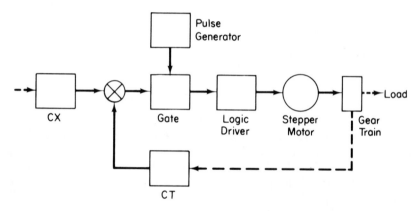

FIG. 12-16. Analog-to-digital Shaft Angle Converter

the feedback loop and any special circuitry used for damping results in quite a savings in design time and installation.

In the closed-loop or positional feedback system, the motor is used like a conventional servo motor. In such a feedback system, a signal from the output is fed back and is used to operate a gate controlling the pulses from a pulse generator. For most applications, the motor must be operated within its response range, the same as with the open-loop system. However, when velocity feedback or a signal similar to velocity feedback is used, the motor can be started in its response range and from there accelerated into its slew range, and amazingly high performance can then be obtained.

NOTE: Much of the material in Sections 12.6 through 12.11 was excerpted by permission from a brochure of Muirhead Instruments Ltd., Stratford, Ontario, Canada.

THIRTEEN

Microprocessors, computers, and servomechanisms

13.1. GENERAL

One of the first servomechanisms to be used commercially was the flyball governor invented by James Watt in 1788 to control the speed of a steam engine automatically. One of the first computers to be used was the abacus invented by the Chinese and, to some extent, still used by them. From the advent of the abacus and the flyball governor to the modern servo and electronic computer, much has happened. The advancement of the electronic art from tubes to transistors and integrated circuits has provided the control industry with equipment and measuring instrumentation giving increased precision, reliability and economy. Computers, both analog and especially digital, are used more and more to achieve the ultimate in performance in systems where many variables are measured and controlled simultaneously.

Even though we think of computers as being all electronic, and we know that their central processors are, modern computer systems also incorporate a large amount of electromechanical instrumentation. The interfaces for instrumentation such as printers, tape drives, computer peripherals, and control transducers require very precise control devices which can control with high precision the incremental motion required. Some of these transducers may be synchros, resolvers, LVDT's, and different types of servo motors, especially the stepper motor. Figure 13-1 is a typical block diagram of a dc velocity servo system being commanded by binary words on two parallel lines with each of the words denoting increment size and direction respectively. This system has the usual servo

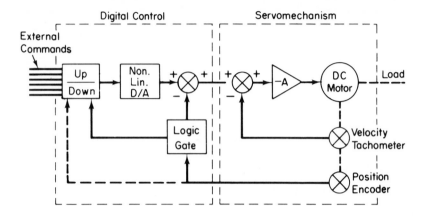

FIG. 13-1. Digital Control of a dc Servo System

components plus a digital and velocity transducer and a digital up/down counter with its associated circuitry.

The typical sequence of events that takes place after a single increment input is as follows: The single word input is entered into an up/down counter whose output is then decoded and fed into a nonlinear digital to analog converter. From the converter, the signal is fed to a dc velocity or rate servo whose permanent magnet motor then accelerates, driving its load and the position encoder. The position encoder then feeds into the gate and the up/down counter until the number counts down to its predetermined value. When this value is reached, the signal to the amplifier decreases, and the motor decelerates. The velocity tachometer (tachometer-generator) is also driven by the dc motor, and it feeds a signal proportional to speed to the servo summing junction for stabilization purposes.

13.2. THE MINICOMPUTER

The use of digital electronics in control has probably grown the fastest in the process and machine tool industry chiefly because of the advent of the minicomputer. The development of the minicomputer really came about because one company, Digital Equipment Corporation, did not believe that, for a computer, bigger and faster was necessarily better. Instead, they came out with a computer that could be sold to those in the industrial field who could not afford the high cost of the larger computer. Minicomputers now give a large number of users enormous computing power at relatively low cost. As the prices drop, it becomes more and more economically feasible to use them in greater varieties of applications.

Some people believe that there will be a computer in every home within a decade.

The typical minicomputer is a small (about the size of a portable television set), general purpose, digital computer that is capable of providing a minimum of 4k (4096 words) bits of programmable memory with associated power supply, teletypewriter, programmer console and related hardware; it sells for about $20,000. The initial application of a minicomputer was in the engineering and scientific field where it supplemented the technician in the control of experiments and tests and in instantaneous data reduction and interpretation. Analytical instrumentation and research in the fields of gas chromatography, crystallography, geophysics, wind tunnel testing, cardiology, spectroscopy, etc., are ideal places for the minicomputer. However, since research and development is somewhat stable, this field became somewhat saturated; therefore, the minicomputer moved into the industrial control field.

In the industrial control field, minicomputers have had wide acceptance in industries where (1) labor costs are a large factor in the total cost picture, (2) close tolerances of products are required, and (3) many complex variables are involved. In these areas, the minicomputer outshines the large process computers mainly because it is being used as a local-loop controller feeding data into a larger data-processing computer. Minicomputers are being used extensively in the small, discrete parts manufacturing industries where production control, storage, and expediting and shipping problems are becoming more acute. Other areas of use in industrial control are automotive testing and checking, automatic inventory control, electrical component testing, production-line control and scheduling, numerically controlled machine tools, and data acquisition and reduction. One of the largest areas of use will be in the data communications field where, for example, messages are switched between terminals or points, or where an exchange of information will take place between remote terminals and a central process computer. The one thing that has probably made the minicomputer so much in demand is the decreasing cost of its *heart, i.e.,* central processor unit (CPU), even though the peripheral equipment used to make up a complete system has not declined in price very much.

13.3. THE MICROPROCESSOR

The microprocessor, which moved out of the laboratories in 1973, will begin to take its place in the digital electronics field in the future and may well be the most important advance since the transistor was developed. The microprocessor may be likened to a minicomputer with a different

CPU unit fabricated on one tiny piece of silicon that gives all the advantages of digital computing techniques at an order of magnitude lower in price. The heart of the microprocessor is its central processing unit that is made up of large scale integration (LSI) circuitry and that has the ability to process both arithmetic and logic data in a program control mode. It has filled a gap in the industrial control field for those low-cost applications where the relatively large and costly software requirements of the minicomputer are not necessary. Thus, all the advantages of a computer are realized through microprocessors without the attendant disadvantage of using or developing such software. Programs must be developed and debugged beforehand, although they are easier to do because of the microprocessor's four-bit design and ease with which it can handle BCD arithmetic. Thus, the general application area for a microprocessor lies between the minicomputer and those devices which use LSI circuitry such as the four-function, hand-held calculator. Because of its small size, low

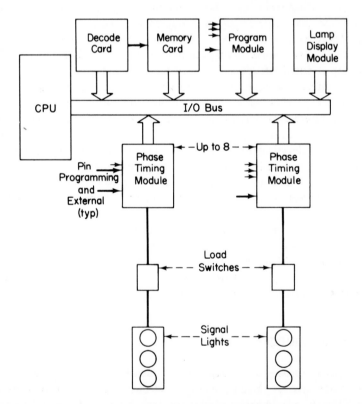

FIG. 13-2. Traffic Control through a Minicomputer (Courtesy of Chilton Technological Seminars, Radnor, Pa.)

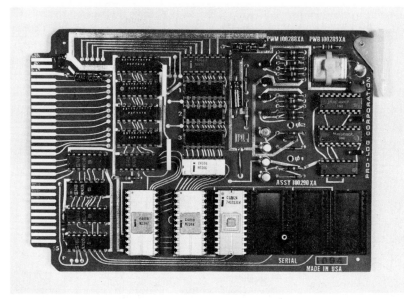

FIG. 13-3. A Microprocessor (Courtesy of Pro-Log Corporation, Monterey, Calif.)

power consumption, and reliability, the microprocessor will be ideally suited for use in appliances such as electric stoves, automatic washers and dryers, and refrigerators as well as in automobiles, cash registers, etc.

One very large field, that is now 75% controlled through electro-mechanical relays and controllers, is traffic control. In this field, the microprocessor will probably act as the CPU for a more complex computer. Figure 13-2 shows a block diagram of such a computer controller. This system can be easily changed to fit special traffic conditions or laws by simply using different software because all that is really needed here is counting and simple bit manipulation. As traffic moves more efficiently through intersections, less energy is wasted with attendant reduction in pollution.

In reality, the microprocessor consists of control and arithmetic, and it is the heart of a digital subsystem known as a *microprogrammable processor* or *microcomputer*. A microprocessor is pictured in figure 13-3. Many semiconductor manufacturers now offer the microprocessor as a standard digital logic building block which will allow the system designer to design the required control system. In many of these control applications, a piece of hardware performs a certain job over and over on demand with little data acquisition. Every job is usually unique which means no canned program. It may be for a high volume market or for a

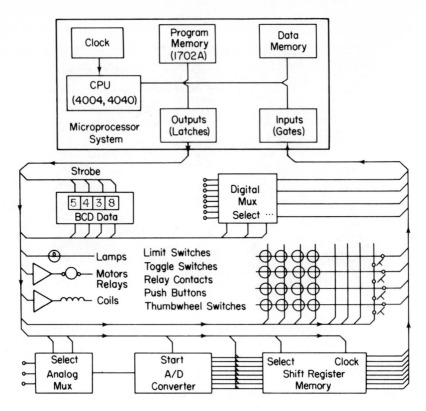

FIG. 13-4. Control System Showing a Microprocessor as a Logic Element with Different Loads (Courtesy of Pro-Log Corporation, Monterey, Calif.)

one-of-a-kind nature. Two characteristics are inherent in control of this nature, *i.e.*, (1) when the power is turned on, the system does the job, and (2) all hardware of the system is necessary to do that job.

Figure 13-4 shows a microprocessor system used as a logic element to supply different types of loads. Here, it is treated as a black box with a number of input gates and output latching drivers. These I/O's are wired to loads which might be switch contacts (relay contacts, keys, thumbwheel switches, push buttons, relay coils, lamps, motors, etc.), and which are then wired in a matrix configuration where one axis is driven by the outputs, and the other axis is sensed by the inputs. Functions and information of these loads are all given in the program. The microprocessor can thus perform timing sequences, make decisions, convert codes, analyze and linearize curves, do arithmetic, etc. When used in this manner, the microprocessor eliminates component wiring (which other systems require), and it instead has specific coding put into the Program Memory

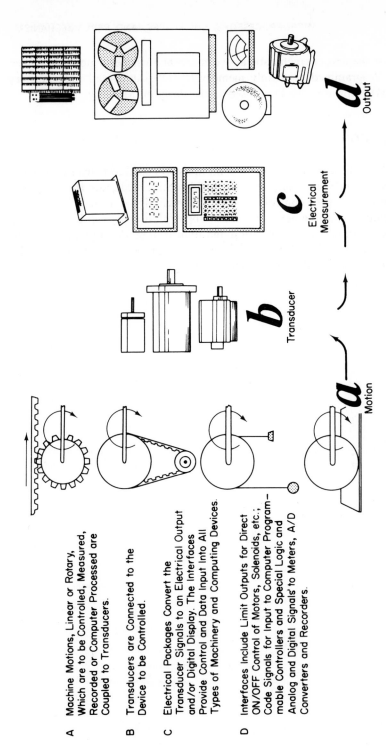

A   Machine Motions, Linear or Rotary, Which are to be Controlled, Measured, Recorded or Computer Processed are Coupled to Transducers.

B   Transducers are Connected to the Device to be Controlled.

C   Electrical Packages Convert the Transducer Signals to an Electrical Output and/or Digital Display. The Interfaces Provide Control and Data Input Into All Types of Machinery and Computing Devices.

D   Interfaces Include Limit Outputs for Direct ON/OFF Control of Motors, Solenoids, etc.; Code Signals for Input to Computer Programmable Controllers and Special Logic and Analog and Digital Signals' to Meters, A/D Converters and Recorders.

a Motion   *b* Transducer   *c* Electrical Measurement   *d* Output

FIG. 13-5. The A-B-C-D's of Industrial/Computer Control (Courtesy of Astrosystems, Inc., Lake Success, N. Y.)

so that the first characteristic above is satisfied whenever power is turned on. Programmed read only memory (PROM) and read only memory (ROM) chips are coded and used as the Program Memory.

13.4. CONCLUSION

Microprocessors and microcomputers will establish themselves more and more in the electronic and industrial control fields, and they may play a larger part in the control of a servo through digital means. There is no question that whole new, specialized application areas will be opened up in the consumer, communication and industrial sectors provided that the support and software for these applications can be married. Figure 13-5 illustrates the A-B-C-D's of such a marriage.

FOURTEEN

Laboratory experiments

14.1. GENERAL

This chapter is made up of a number of laboratory experiments designed to give the student or reader a thorough understanding of elementary servo principles using one of the modular servo trainers that are illustrated and discussed in Chapter 11. Each experiment will take about two hours to perform and another two to three hours to write up, should that be required. The experiments should be done in the order listed as each succeeding experiment is more complex and depends on information learned from the previous one.

14-2. TITLE: DC SERVO MOTOR CHARACTERISTICS

OBJECT: To investigate and to take measurements of dc servo motor characteristics, to calibrate a dc tachometer-generator, and to record the steady-state and transient response of the motor

APPARATUS: Modular servo system trainer, VTVM, dc oscilloscope or recorder

PROCEDURE:

I. MOTOR OPERATION

1. Mount the servo amplifier, the power supply, and the motor on the steel baseboard. Plug the motor into the servo amplifier and the servo amplifier into the power supply. See figure 14-2.

2. Connect one of the potentiometers in the attenuator unit across the dc supply with the slider being connected to input terminal

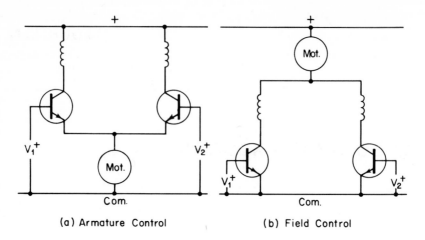

(a) Armature Control   (b) Field Control

FIG. 14-1. Motor Connections

No. 1 of the servo amplifier. This will provide a variable input to the motor through the amplifier.

3. Connect the motor so that armature control of the motor will be obtained. See figure 14-1(a).

4. Set the potentiometer to give zero volts. Turn the power supply on and the meter should read about 0.5 ampere. This is due to basic circuits in the servo amplifier, and it does not affect the motor connections. Turn the potentiometer up, and, when the current has increased to about one ampere, the motor should start with the speed being controlled by the voltage from the potentiometer. When voltage is applied to the other servo amplifier input jack, the motor will reverse its direction of rotation.

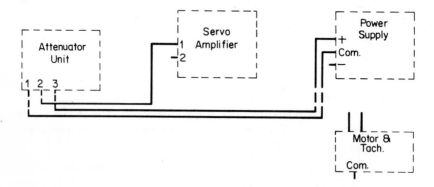

FIG. 14-2. Motor Experiment

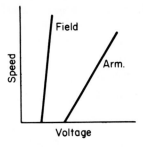

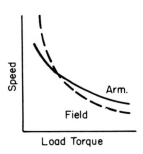

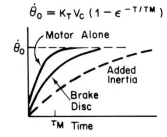

$$\dot{\theta}_0 = K_T V_C \, (1 - \epsilon^{-T/T_M})$$

$\dot{\theta}_0$ = Velocity

V_C = Volts

K_T = Speed/Volts Applied

τ_M = Motor Time Constant

FIG. 14-3. Motor Characteristics

5. Record the voltage at which the motor just starts to rotate, for both directions of rotation, by measuring the voltage at the input to the servo amplifier.

II. TACHOMETER-GENERATOR CALIBRATION—K_G FACTOR

1. The motor speed may be computed from the tachometer-generator voltage once the factor K_G regulating speed and emf has been found. To determine this factor (which is measured in volts/1000 rpm), the motor must be driven at a known speed and the tachometer-generator output must be measured. Determine K_G by using a strobotach.

III. MEASUREMENT OF MOTOR CHARACTERISTICS

1. (a) *Armature Connection—Speed* vs. *Voltage*—Increase the potentiometer voltage until the motor just starts, *record this*, and then record output of the tachometer as indicated on the voltmeter for six settings of the potentiometer between the starting point and 10. Measure input voltage at the servo amplifier for each of these points. See figure 14-3(a).

To obtain the *speed-torque* characteristic, locate the magnet brake assembly correctly and then set the brake to maximum (10), and increase the input voltage to maximum. Leave the input voltage constant and swing the brake back taking readings of tachometer voltage for five settings of the brake between 2 and 10. See figure 14-3(b).

2. *Field Connection—Speed* vs. *Voltage*—Arrange the field connection (see figure 14-1,b); then swing the brake magnet clear. Increase input voltage slowly until the motor just starts and record potentiometer setting. Increase the potentiometer setting until the tachometer output is 5V and note this setting. If possible, repeat for a tachometer output of 9V. Again see figure 14-3(a). Set the brake to maximum and adjust the input to give maximum current. Keep the input constant and swing the brake back taking readings of tachometer voltage for five settings of the brake between 2 and 10. Again see figure 14-3(b).

IV. Transient response of motor

1. Connect the motor for armature control with no disc on the output shaft. Using a servo analyzer or function generator, apply a square wave of about 6–8V amplitude at a frequency of 0.15 Hz to one servo amplifier input jack (the potentiometer voltage input may be disconnected or reduced to its lowest value). The motor will now respond to the positive half wave.

2. The change in the speed increase of the motor may be examined by connecting the tachometer-generator output to a dc oscilloscope or recorder. An exponential rise will be observed. Note the difference in response time for the following cases:

   1. no brake disc
   2. brake disc only
   3. brake disc under load
   4. inertia disc

See figure 14-3(c).

3. Connect the tachometer-generator output to one input of the two channel recorder and make a trace of the speed characteristic with the brake disc mounted.

4. If time permits, mount the inertia disc on the low speed output shaft and note effect of the gear train between the motor and the load.

RESULTS

1. Make a simple block diagram for the motor connection shown in the Procedure, part III, step 1.

2. Determine the factor K_G and then plot speed *vs.* input volts for both connections of part III. Also plot speed *vs.* brake scale for both sets of readings.

3. From the recorded trace of the transient response, determine the motor time constant (it should be about 0.25 s).

4. It may be said that the armature connection requires more driving power. However, it is easier to control whereas the field connection is more sensitive but less desirable in a servo system in relation to the system stability. Which set of curves shows this to be true? Why?

5. What effect does the inertia load have on motor response? Why?

6. Is the system shown in Procedure, part III (Results 1) an open-loop or closed-loop system? Why?

7. Which method of control, armature or field, will have the higher gain? Why?

14-3.   TITLE: DC SERVO MOTOR SPEED CONTROL SYSTEM

OBJECT: To investigate a simple speed control system with its associated operational amplifier and preamplifier, to determine tachometer-generator polarity, and to ascertain the effect of forward path gain on performance

APPARATUS: Modular servo system trainer, VTVM, dc oscilloscope, recorder

PROCEDURE:

I.   PROPERTIES OF AN OPERATIONAL AMPLIFIER

1.   Connect the $\pm$ dc supplies and set the control switch to the left position. Measure the output which ideally should be zero, and adjust the zero switch, if necessary. Connect the two potentiometers in the attenuator unit across the dc supplies so that two independent variable voltages, V1 and V2, are available at the sliders. Connect the sliders to two of the inputs as is shown in figure 14-4(a) and set each slider to 2.5V so that 5V output is obtained. The output of the amplifier can now be checked. It should sum the inputs, but with a reversed sign. Do this in three steps for the polarities as shown.

     1. V_1 POS. V_2 POS.

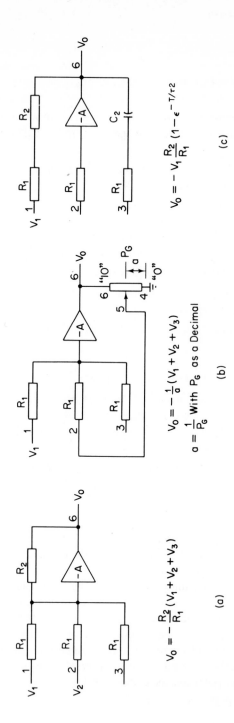

$$V_0 = -\frac{R_2}{R_1}(V_1 + V_2 + V_3)$$

(a)

$$V_0 = -\frac{1}{a}(V_1 + V_2 + V_3)$$

$$a = \frac{1}{P_G} \text{ With } P_G \text{ as a Decimal}$$

(b)

$$V_0 = -V_1\frac{R_2}{R_1}(1-\epsilon^{-T/\tau 2})$$

(c)

FIG. 14-4. Operational Amplifier Circuits

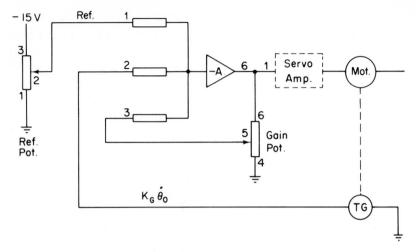

FIG. 14-5. Speed Control System

    2. V_1 POS. V_2 NEG.
    3. V_1 NEG. V_2 NEG.

2. Set the control switch to "EXT. FDBK." Connect the gain control potentiometer in the attenuator unit to the amplifier output with the slider being connected back to one of the input jacks as is shown in figure 14-4(b). Apply 2V to one input jack and measure the output to check that the gain is inversely proportional to the output potentiometer setting, *i.e.*, for 50% setting, the output should be 4V for a gain of 2. Do this in four steps for the following settings.

    1. 25% setting
    2. 50% setting
    3. 75% setting
    4. 90% setting

II.   SIMPLE SPEED CONTROL SYSTEM

1. Connect the attenuator unit, operational amplifier, servo amplifier, power supply, and motor/tachometer-generator units as is shown in figure 14-5. Arrange the motor for armature control and swing the brake clear. Set the gain of the operational amplifier to unity by setting the gain potentiometer to 100%. *DO NOT* connect in the tachometer-generator. Check to see that if the reference potentiometer is turned up, the motor will rotate. Set the operational amplifier switch to normal (CCW).

2. In order for the system to operate properly, the tachometer-generator polarity must be checked. The output of the tachometer must oppose the reference voltage at the input. Ground one side of the tachometer and then connect the other side to an operational amplifier input. If the speed decreases, then negative feedback is obtained; if the speed increases to a very high value, then positive feedback is obtained. Finally, connect the tachometer for *negative feedback*.

III. EFFECT OF FORWARD GAIN ON SYSTEM PERFORMANCE

1. As the forward gain is increased, the speed drop for a given load should decrease. This is so because the power to the amplifier increases with gain.

2. Be sure the tachometer-generator is connected for negative feedback. Adjust the reference voltage to give a speed of 1000 rpm with the operational amplifier gain set to 1.0 and the brake swung clear.

3. Swing the brake forward and then measure (1) motor input voltage at the servo amplifier, and (2) motor speed (via tachometer voltage). Do not adjust the reference potentiometer while taking these readings.

4. Repeat part III, step 3 for operational amplifier gains of 5 and 10, each time readjusting the reference voltage to give a no-load speed of 1000 rpm. When motor current approaches a value of 2A, the speed may fall quite rapidly as load is increased. This shows that the maximum power that can be supplied depends on system capacity and not on feedback.

IV. REVERSIBLE SPEED CONTROL

1. Insert the preamplifier unit instead of the operational amplifier in the circuit of figure 14-6 and connect the reference potentiometer across the ± dc supplies as is shown. Arrange the motor for armature connection and swing the brake clear. Connect the reference voltage and tachometer-generator output to the preamplifier. Be sure the tachometer is connected to give *negative feedback*.

2. Adjust the speed to 1000 rpm at no load. Be sure that the motor is running in the same direction as it previously was.

3. Swing the brake forward and perform the same test as in part III, step 3. Check that the drop in speed is much less because the amplifier gain is about 25 rather than 10 (see figure 14-7).

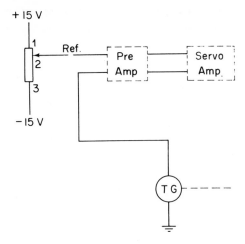

FIG. 14-6. Reversible Speed Control

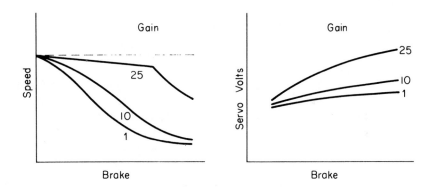

FIG. 14-7. Speed Control Characteristics

RESULTS

1. Make a simple block diagram for the motor connection of the Procedure, part I.

2. Plot speed versus brake setting for the load tests for gains of 1, 10 and 25. On a separate graph sheet, plot motor input volts versus brake setting for the same load tests.

3. Why was it so important to determine the correct polarity tachometer-generator for system operation?

4. The curves show that as the forward gain of the operational amplifier is increased the amount of error required to drive the system decreases. Why? Also prove by formula.

5. What is the main purpose of the operational amplifier?

6. What two benefits resulted in the system operation when the pre-amplifier was used?

7. Show by formula and calculation that the results of Procedure, part I, steps 1 and 2 came out as expected.

14-4.   TITLE: DC SERVO SPEED AND POSITION CONTROL SYSTEM

OBJECT: To investigate the behavior of a speed control system under various operating conditions, and to set up the error channel that is associated with a mechanical position control system, closing the loop, and general performance characteristics such as deadband

APPARATUS: Modular servo system trainer, dc oscilloscope, VTVM, recorder (if needed)

PROCEDURE:

I.   INVESTIGATION—MOTOR SPEED CONTROL BEHAVIOR

1.   Connect the attenuator unit, operational amplifier, preamplifier, servo amplifier, the input potentiometer, power supply, and motor/tachometer-generator unit as is shown in figure 14-8. Arrange for armature control. Set the gain potentiometer in the attenuator unit to zero, the input potentiometer to zero, and the velocity potentiometer to 10. Switch the power "on" and adjust the preamplifier zero to get a minimum reading on the ammeter.

2.   Set the operational amplifier switch to normal (CCW) and then set the gain potentiometer to 10. Remove the lead from the velocity potentiometer to socket 3 on the operational amplifier and adjust the operational amplifier zero to get a minimum reading on the ammeter. Reconnect the lead to socket 3 and adjust the input potentiometer until the motor stops. The input potentiometer should be at zero.

3.   Set the gain and tachometer potentiometers to 10. Using a servo analyzer, apply a square wave of $\pm 3V$ at 0.2 Hz at socket 2 of the operational amplifier. Display the velocity signal (output of the tachometer-generator) and the error signal (output of the operational amplifier) on a dual-channel scope. The display should be as shown in figure 14-9(a); also note the ammeter reading.

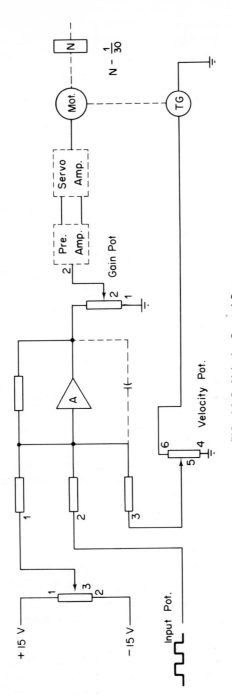

FIG. 14-8. Velocity Control System

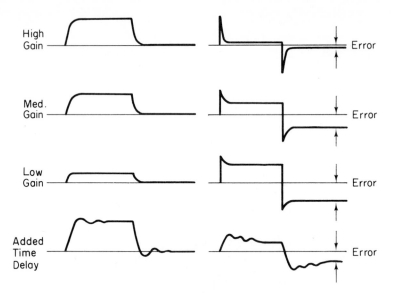

FIG. 14-9. Velocity Control Signals

4. Reduce the gain to 5 and repeat step 3. Reduce gain to 1 and repeat step 3.

5. Introduce an additional time delay in the forward path by setting the switch on the operational amplifier to the center position. Repeat the display of the tachometer and error with the gain potentiometer at 10. See figure 14-9(b).

6. Set the selector switch on the operational amplifier to the normal position, tachometer potentiometer at 0 and gain potentiometer at 10. Fit the brake assembly and adjust it until the tachometer display is the same size as was seen in step 3. Note the ammeter readings.

II. DETERMINING DEADBAND

1. Disconnect the square wave from the operational amplifier so that the motor is controlled from the input potentiometer only.

2. Measure deadband by finding the *total angle* through which the motor just starts to rotate in either direction. Start with the gain at 1.0.

   NOTE: The deadband width can be determined ahead of time. In section 14-2, Procedure, part III, the minimum voltage to start the motor rotating was found (approximately 5V). The

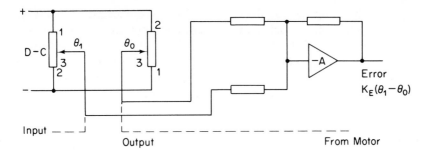

FIG. 14-10. Error Channel Connections

preamplifier gain is about 25; therefore, the minimum voltage at the input to the preamplifier should be about ± 0.2V. With gain at 1.0, then about ± 2V will be required at the output of the operational amplifier. If the position error constant is about 0.1 volt/deg, then $\pm 20°$ are required to give ± 2V for a total deadband width of about 40°. The deadband should be equal around the zero position; if it is not, adjust the preamplifier zero until it is.

3. Repeat this deadband test for gains of 2, 5, 8 and 10.

III. THE ERROR CHANNEL AND CLOSING THE LOOP

1. Disconnect the lead from the tachometer potentiometer to the operational amplifier. Also disconnect the input to the pre-amplifier. Set the gain potentiometer at 0.

2. Mount the output potentiometer on the motor shaft extension and then connect to the $\pm$ dc supply as is shown in figure 14-10. Connect the slider to an input of the operational amplifier as is shown.

3. Set the control switch of the operational amplifier to give normal addition. Measure the voltages between each potentiometer slider and *common*, and turn the shafts until zero voltage is obtained. Both dials should be at or about zero. If they are not, then zero them.

4. The output of the operational amplifier should now be zero. Rotate the input shaft and check that this output depends on shaft displacement. Determine the position error constant, K_{PE}; it should be about 0.1 volt/deg, *i.e.*, a shaft displacement of 10° should give 1V error.

5. Reconnect the lead from the operational amplifier to the pre-amplifier. Introduce a small displacement between the input

shaft and the output shaft, say 30°. Now increase gain slowly. If the output shaft moves *toward* the input, the connections are correct. If the output shaft moves in the reverse direction or settles (oscillates) at 180°, then reverse either the leads to the servo amplifier and/or the $\pm$ connections to the output potentiometer. The system should now align.

RESULTS

1. Make a simple block diagram for the motor connection of the speed control system.

2. Explain why the deadband decreased as the gain was increased.

3. In setting up the error channel, Procedure, part III, if the input and output potentiometers are connected in reverse to the dc supplies, the output potentiometer will lock 180° out of phase to the input potentiometer. Why is this true?

4. How did the *measured* position error constant, K_{PE}, compare to the predicted value? Show how this is found?

5. In the speed control system, the displays indicated that the transient error was the same for all values of gain, but that the steady-state error increased as the gain was decreased. Why is this true?

6. When the additional time delay was introduced, the speed response showed that the motor now oscillated as well as the error. Why is this true?

7. Explain how the error is found in the speed control system and where it is displayed.

14-5.   TITLE: TESTING OF A DC SERVO POSITION-CONTROL SYSTEM

OBJECT: To investigate the reduction of overshoot and settling time through velocity feedback of a mechanical position-control system, the effect of added inertia, and the stabilization of the control system

APPARATUS: Modular servo system trainer, dc oscilloscope with four-trace plug-in, and recorder

PROCEDURE:

I.   REDUCTION OF OVERSHOOT AND SETTLING TIME—VELOCITY FEEDBACK

1.   The complete mechanical position control system with the command and output potentiometers mounted and connected to the dc supplies and the operational amplifier is shown in figure 14-11. The output of the operational amplifier which is

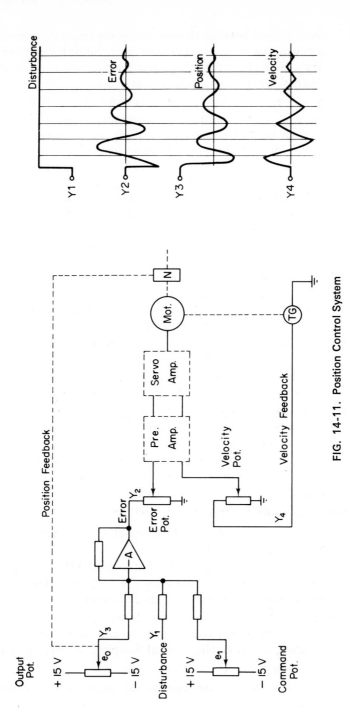

FIG. 14-11. Position Control System

the difference between these two, *i.e.*, the error, is connected to a potentiometer in the attenuator unit and to the preamplifier. The output from the tachometer-generator is also fed to the preamplifier through a potentiometer.

2. As can be seen, this system contains two feedback loops—the outer loop through the error potentiometer and the inner loop through the tachometer-generator. In order for the system to operate properly, the polarities of both loops must be considered separately. Set both the error and velocity potentiometers to zero and then proceed in the following manner:

Error Potentiometer—The correct polarity was determined in section 14-4, part III, under the section on Closing the Loop; therefore, refer to this section.

Velocity Potentiometer—With this potentiometer at zero, start the motor rotating by turning the preamplifier zero adjustment. Increase the velocity potentiometer setting, and, if the polarity of the tachometer-generator is correct, the speed should decrease. If it does not, then reverse the connections to the tachometer-generator. Rezero the preamplifier.

3. To determine the effect of velocity feedback, set the gain of the error potentiometer to 10 and then turn the command shaft sharply through about 45° for several different settings of the velocity potentiometer. Observe the results.

4. Using a servo analyzer, apply a square wave of about $\pm 3V$ at 0.2 Hz to the input of the operational amplifier. Display the signal of the output potentiometer and the error on a storage scope, channels 1 and 2. Examine and record the position response and error signal for various velocity potentiometer settings.

II. EFFECT OF ADDED INERTIA AND/OR TIME DELAY

1. Mount the inertia disc on the motor shaft and repeat the test of part I, step 4.

2. Mount the inertia disc on the shaft opposite the output potentiometer and repeat the test of part II, section 1. Note carefully any differences in the form of the responses.

3. Remove the inertia disc and switch in the additional time delay in the operational amplifier. Investigate the response for zero damping, underdamping, critical damping, and overdamping.

III. STABILIZATION

1. Set the switch on the operational amplifier to the normal position.

2. Connect the four-trace plug-in of the storage scope to the four "Y" signal points. Be sure the trigger switch is "out" so that the time base will internally trigger on channel 1. Set the CHOP-ALT switch to CHOP.

3. Set the gain potentiometer at 10 and then investigate the response for zero damping, underdamping, critical damping, and over-damping. Record these displays. Note that the velocity feedback signal is in opposition to the error signal. Also note that these signals will cancel shortly before the error goes through zero.

4. Change the disturbance to a sine wave at 0.1 Hz. Record the variation in amplitude and phase shift between the signal and the position signal as the frequency is slowly increased to 5 Hz.

IV. FIELD CONTROL

1. Disconnect the disturbance signal to the operational amplifier. Change the motor wiring to give field control.

2. Investigate the behavior of the system for small angular inputs to the input potentiometer for various levels of gain and velocity feedback.

RESULTS

1. Make a block diagram for this complete system showing all polarities.

2. Most servo motors are built with a relatively long armature and small diameter. Did any of the results of this experiment show why this is true?

3. What is meant by the term "velocity feedback," and why does it stabilize a system so effectively.

4. Was there any difference in the operation of the system when the additional time delay element of the operational amplifier was switched "in" or "out"? What is the difference due to?

5. What was the difference in the position signal when a sinusoidal command was used rather than a step-position command, especially as the command frequency was increased to a value of 3.0 to 5.0 Hz?

6. Is the following error, i.e., angular lag between input and output, affected by changes in level of tachometer feedback?

7. What are the advantages and disadvantages of using field control for the motor?

8. In Procedure, part III, step 3, a statement was made that velocity and error canceled shortly before the error went through zero. Was this true and why?

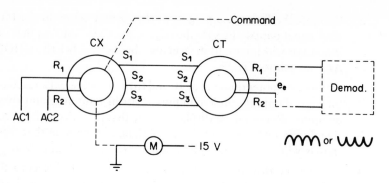

FIG. 14-12. Synchro Link

14-6. TITLE: A DC POSITION CONTROL SERVO USING
        AC ERROR DETECTORS

OBJECT: To study and to investigate the operation of continuous rotation
    transducers in the error channel and the conversion of an amplitude-
    modulated ac error signal to a dc error signal through a demodulator

APPARATUS: Modular servo system trainer, synchro units, demodulator,
    dc oscilloscope or recorder

PROCEDURE:

I. SYNCHRO LINK

1. Mount the synchros and the power supply. Connect the
   synchros in cyclic connection. Connect R1 and R2 of the
   synchro transmitter to the ac output of the power supply.
   Connect the −15V supply to the −15V terminal of the small
   dc drive motor of the transmitter (see figure 14-12).

2. Set the dial on the transmitter to 0° and monitor the output at
   R1 of the synchro transformer on an oscilloscope. Ground R2
   of the CT. Note dial settings of the CT for both minimum and
   maximum outputs.

3. Drive the transmitter rotor at various speeds by means of the dc
   drive control and monitor the output of the CT. In order to
   observe the change in phase each time the amplitude of the
   signal goes through zero, it will be necessary to use a very low
   sensitivity setting on the oscilloscope.

II. INVESTIGATION OF DEMODULATOR ACTION

1. Mount the demodulator unit on the baseboard. Connect the
   error output of the synchro CT to input terminals No. 2 and
   No. 4 of the demodulator.

2. Set the drive motor on the transmitter to the "off" position and also the dial to 0°. Monitor the waveform at terminal 9 of the demodulator and adjust the CT dial until the error voltage at R1 and R2 is zero. It may be necessary to use the zero control on the demodulator to get this zero output at terminal 9.

3. Measure output voltage at R1 for different dial settings, *i.e.*, 0°, 30°, 45°, 60° and 90°.

4. Change the dial of the CT until maximum output is obtained at R1. Adjust the phase control on the demodulator until the output at terminal No. 9 is one of the signals that are shown in figure 14-12. Be sure that the filter switch is "off."

5. Note the variation in the demodulator output as the motor driving the transmitter is varied in speed. Note the variations in output as the filter in the demodulator is switched in, *i.e.*, filter switch to demodulator.

III. CLOSED-LOOP SYNCHRO ERROR LINK

1. Connect the power supply, the servo amplifier, the preamplifier, the attenuator unit, the modulator/demodulator, the motor, and the synchros as is shown in figure 14-13.

2. Set the gain and tachometer potentiometers to 0. Energize the system and adjust the zero control on the preamplifier so the motor does not run.

Set the dial on the transmitter so that it is about 30° different from the CT. Monitor the output at terminal No. 9 of the demodulator. Set the filter switch to "off" and adjust the phase control until the output shows a good full wave rectified ac. Now reset the filter switch to demod.

3. Set the gain to 5 and note system response.

4. Switch the drive motor of the synchro transmitter to "on" and adjust it until the transmitter rotates at about 1 rps. (This may be determined by visually watching the 60 Hz track on the dial.) Note system response for the following settings:

   (a) Gain—5   Velocity—1 5 10
   (b) Gain—1 5 10   Velocity—5
   (c) Synchro transmitter—0 rps
       Gain—5   Velocity—1 5 10

5. Mount the output potentiometer to the low speed motor shaft and connect it to the ± dc supply. Apply the disturbance signal (square wave) between the external input and common on the demodulator. Monitor the output from the wiper of the output

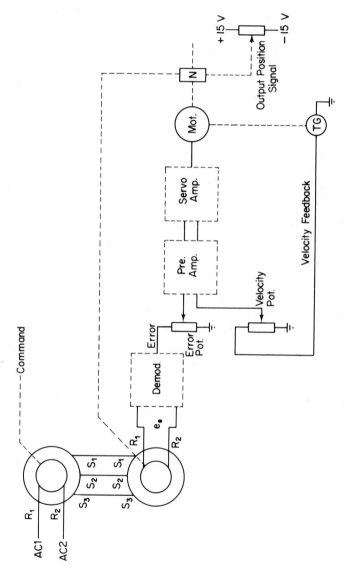

FIG. 14-13. Position Control—Synchro Link

potentiometer. Investigate the response of the system for the same settings of the gain and velocity potentiometers as in part III, step 4.

RESULTS

1. Make a block diagram for this system.
2. In the setup used, what changes the ac signal to the dc signal that is is needed to drive the servo motor?
3. From observations made while conducting the experiment, which feedback stabilizes the system the best? Why? How does this answer compare with the theoretical answer?
4. Does the combination of ac and dc have any adverse effect on the system as compared with a system that is only dc?
5. What may have been a cause for the instability at the low end of the frequency range (0.1 to 1.0 Hz)?
6. In the performance of this system in part III, was there any time where the false null of the synchro would have an effect on the output? Explain!

14-7. TITLE: A RELAY-CONTROLLED POSITION-CONTROL SYSTEM

OBJECT: To study and to analyze the characteristics of a servo relay unit and the effect that the relay output has on a mechanical position-control system

APPARATUS: Modular servo system trainer, simulated relay unit, and dc oscilloscope

PROCEDURE:

I. SIMULATED RELAY UNIT

1. Connect the simulated relay unit as is shown in figure 14-14 and apply a triangle (ramp) wave of 1 or 2 Hz; observe and record the characteristics for the following relays.

Ideal	Set the width and hysteresis potentiometers to zero and switches S_1 to deadband and S_2 to hysteresis.
Deadband	Adjust width potentiometer so that deadband appears.
Hysteresis	Set width potentiometer to zero and adjust hysteresis potentiometer so that hysteresis appears.

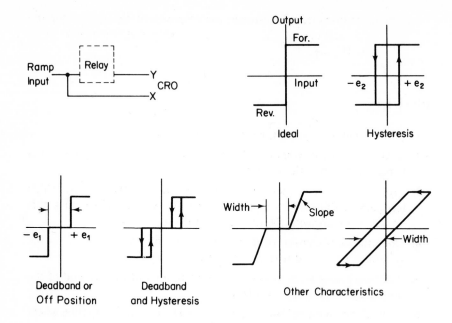

FIG. 14-14. Characteristics of a Relay System

Hysteresis and deadband	Adjust both controls.
Limiting with adjustable slope and deadband	Set S_2 to slope. Adjust width and slope control for both directions for normal deadband and maximum slope.
Backlash	Set S_1 to backlash. Adjust width control.

II.　RELAY-OPERATED SYSTEM—OPEN LOOP

1. Connect the following modular units as is shown in figure 14-15: attenuator, operational amplifier, preamplifier, servo amplifier, power supply, relay, input and output potentiometers, and motor with the motor arranged for armature control. Set gain, width and hysteresis potentiometers to zero and disconnect the feedback line from the output potentiometer. Adjust the input potentiometer to mid scale.

2. Turn up the gain control until the motor starts to rotate. The direction of rotation can now be controlled by CW or CCW rotation of the input potentiometer with this reversal being very sharp, indicating an ideal relay characteristic.

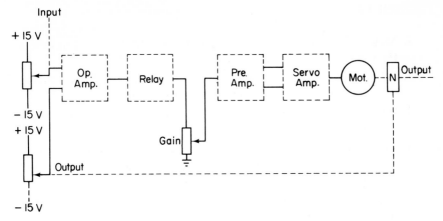

FIG. 14-15. Connections of a Relay-controlled System

3. Set S_1 and S_2 to deadband and hysteresis respectively. Then for various settings of the width and hysteresis potentiometers, observe and record the effect on the output potentiometer as the input potentiometer is rotated.

III. RELAY-OPERATED SYSTEM—CLOSED LOOP

1. Reconnect the feedback loop and adjust the controls until the motor rotates. If the output potentiometer follows the input potentiometer then the supply connections are correct. If the output potentiometer does not follow the input potentiometer, determine what must be done to get it to do so.

2. Note how the motor oscillates when the width and hysteresis potentiometers are set at zero. Determine how this oscillation may be eliminated and yet still have the system follow.

3. Apply a square wave of the same amplitude and frequency as the ramp input of Procedure, part I and observe the effects of this disturbance.

4. Reduce the amplitude of the square wave and observe the changes, if any, that this makes.

5. To investigate deadband, remove the square wave and set hysteresis to zero and width to about 25%. Rotate the input potentiometer and note response. Determine how the system accuracy can be improved.

6. To investigate hysteresis, set deadband and hysteresis to zero. Turn up the gain until the system oscillates. Determine how the oscillation frequency can be reduced.

RESULTS

1. Make a block diagram for the closed-loop system indicating where the feedback loop may be opened.

2. Why does the motor reverse direction so abruptly under open-loop conditions when the input potentiometer is adjusted?

3. What characteristic was being exhibited by the system under open-loop conditions for Procedure, part II, step 3?

4. One of the general problems of a relay system is that if oscillations are eliminated, then deadband is increased and accuracy is reduced. Did any of your results prove this? Why?

5. Was there any advantage to introducing hysteresis in the control of this system? Why?

6. What are the differences between deadband and hysteresis? Do they affect each other?

7. What effect does deadband have on system response and gain?

SI (metric) units with English and CGS equivalents

	SI		*ENGLISH*		*CGS*	
Quan	*Unit*	*Symbol*	*Unit*	*Symbol*	*Unit*	*Symbol*
Length	1 meter	m	3.28 feet	ft	100 centimeters	cm
			39.37 inches	in		
Mass	1 kilogram	kg	2.2 pounds	lb	10^3 grams	gm
Time	second	s	second	s	second	s
Area	1 square meter	m^2	10.76 square feet	ft^2	10^4 square centimeters	cm^2
Linear velocity	1 meter per second	m/s	3.28 feet per second	ft/s	100 centimeters per second	cm/s
Force	1 Newton	N	0.225 pounds	lb	10^5 dynes	dyne
Energy or work	1 joule watt-second	J	0.738 foot-pound force	ft-lb f	10^7 dyne-centimeters	dyne-cm
Power	1 watt (joule per second)	W	watt 134×10^{-3} horsepower	W HP	10^7 erg per second	erg/s
Linear acceleration	1 meter per second squared	m/s^2	3.28 feet per second squared	ft/s^2	100 centimeters per second squared	cm/s^2
Torque	1 Newton meter	Nm	0.738 pound-foot 141.9 ounce-inch	lb-ft oz-in	10^7 dyne centimeter	dyne-cm
Moment of inertia	1 kilogram-square meter	$kg\text{-}m^2$	23.7 pound-square feet	$lb\text{-}ft^2$	10^7 gram-square centimeter	$gm\text{-}cm^2$
Electric charge	coulomb	C	coulomb	C	coulomb	C
Electric current	ampere	A	ampere	A	ampere	A
Electric potential	volts	V	volt	V	volt	V
Capacitance	farad	F	farad	F	farad	F
Inductance	henry	H	henry	H	henry	H
Resistance	ohm	Ω	ohm	Ω	ohm	Ω

	Other Useful Units		
Angular position	rad	rad	angular deg
Angular velocity	rad/s	rad/s	1°/second
Angular acceleration	rad/s²	rad/s²	1°/second²
Torque constant	Nm/A	oz-in/A	
Voltage constant	V/rpm	volts/rpm	
Damping constant	Nm/rpm	oz-in/rpm	
Viscous damping	Nm/rad s⁻¹	oz-in/rad s⁻¹	

Glossary of terms

Actuating Signal or Error (E)—Reference input (R) minus the primary feedback (C).

Bandwidth—The range of frequencies of a device within which its performance, with respect to some characteristic, conforms to a specified standard.

Block—A part of a control loop that receives an input signal, processes it, and transmits an output signal; a diagrammatic representation of an element of a servomechanism or feedback control system.

Block Diagram—Simplified system reducing each element to its transfer function and schematically representing it as a block.

Bode Diagram—Open-loop plot of phase angle θ and amplitude ratio $\times$ dB as a function of ω; usually plotted on semilog paper with ω in radians per second, and phase angle in degrees.

Carrier Frequency—Constant frequency upon which useable data is superimposed.

Closed Loop—System where the output is fed back to the input for constant comparison; the complete signal path in a control system that is represented as a group of units that are connected in such a manner that a signal started at any point follows a closed path and can be traced back to that point.

Command (R)—The input that is established or varied by some means external to and independent of the feedback control system under consideration.

Control Accuracy—Degree of correspondence between the controlled variable and the ideal value.

Control Ratio—The frequency response of the controlled variable to the reference input; under linear conditions, this ratio is expressed mathematically as C/R = KG(1 + KGH).

Controlled Variable (C)—The quantity, or conditions, of the controlled system that is directly measured and controlled.

Corner Frequency—Frequency where the open-loop plot of gain versus frequency changes slope; the product of this frequency in radians per second and time constant, τ, in seconds equals units.

Critical Damping—The point at which system damping is great enough to overcome all tendencies to oscillate or where the damping ratio equals one.

Damping—A measure of the restraining force that prevents return to an equilibrium position; the damping ratio is a measure of the amount of damping. Critical damping permits the system to return to equilibrium with no overshoots if there is a damping ratio of 1.0. Overdamping permits a slow return to equilibrium with no overshoots if the damping ratio is greater than 1.0. Underdamping permits a rapid return to equilibrium with overshoots; this results in a settling out period required to reach steady state equilibrium, and is present with a damping ratio less than 1.0.

Damping Ratio (ζ)—Ratio of actual damping to critical damping.

Dead Space or Deadband—Maximum deviation on either side of the point of agreement between input and output for which no corrective action will take place.

Dead Time or Time Delay—A period of delay between two related actions such as the beginning of a change in an input signal and the beginning of a related change in the output.

Dynamic Analysis—The study of control system performance by analyzing the effect of disturbance inputs on the controlled variable or in conditions that affect this variable.

Error (E)—Difference between output and input, or the difference between an actual value and a desired or reference value; in a control loop, this error is driven towards a desired minimum.

Error Detector—The element or group of elements that convert the difference between output and input of a system into usable form.

Error Rate Damping—Method of damping in which an additional signal proportional to the rate of change of error is introduced and added to the error signal for anticipatory purposes.

Forward Loop (Path)—In a feedback control loop, the transmission path from the actuating signal to the output signal.

Frequency Response—Practical or mathematical observation of the ability of the output to follow the input when the input is varied sinusoidally over a given frequency range.

Gain Crossover—Point in the plot of loop ratio at which the magnitude of the loop ratio is unity (Bode diagram).

Gain Crossover Frequency—Frequency at which the open-loop system gain is unity or zero dB.

Gain Margin—The amount by which the magnitude of the loop ratio of stable system is different from unity at phase crossover; it is frequently expressed in decibels (Bode diagram).

Lead or Lag—An advance or delay of the output signal with respect to the input.

Natural Frequency (ω_N)—The frequency at which a disturbed second-order system or component would oscillate with zero or no damping.

Negative Feedback—Subtracting some or all of an output from the input to achieve a desired effect; in amplifiers, used for gain stabilization.

Open Loop—Condition where efforts are made to make an output agree with an input without a direct comparison.

Open-loop System—An open-loop system has no feedback, or it has the feedback loop disconnected at the error summing point.

Phase Angle—A measure of the time by which an output lags or leads an input; measured in degrees for sinusoidal signals.

Phase Crossover Frequency—Frequency at which the open-loop phase shift is a full 180° (Bode diagram).

Phase Margin (θ_M)—The angle of difference between the phase of the loop ratio of a stable system and 180° at gain crossover (Bode diagram).

Rate Generator—A signal which changes linearly with time.

Reference Input (R)—The reference used to compare the measured variable to define a deviation of error signal; also referred to as set point or desired value.

Response Time—Time required for the output of a system or element to reach a specified value after the application of a step input or disturbance.

Rise Time—The time required for the output of a system or element to increase from one specified percentage of the final value to another after the application of a step input; usually, the specified percentages are 10% and 90%.

Sensitivity—Maximum possible difference between output and input for which no corrective action will take place.

Servoamplifier—Linear amplifier specifically designed to link error detector voltage to motor control phase at a higher voltage and power level than that supplied by the error detector.

Servomotor—1. Any motor used in a servomechanism to correct physically differences between input and output. 2. Two-phase motor specifically designed for servo applications and having low torque-to-inertia ratio, sloping speed-to-torque curve, and torque proportional to product of the voltage on each phase.

Servomechanism—A system in which the output is mechanically driven by the difference between the input and the output for the purpose of making the output agree with the input.

Settling Time—The time required for the absolute value of the difference between the output of a system or element and its final value to decline below and remain less than a specified amount after the application of a step input or disturbance; the specified amount is often expressed in terms of percent of the final value.

Stability—The property of a system or element that makes its response to a stimulus die down if the stimulus is removed; a statement that a system is stable means that the system is stable under all normal operating conditions and for all types of stimuli normally encountered. A system may be referred to as being stable in one region of operation and not in another. If this is the case, the region of stability should be specified.

Steady State—A stabilized condition in which the output has leveled out, or has reached a constant rate of change, for a constant input; the terminology is also applied to a condition in which the input is a periodic constant amplitude signal.

Steady-state Error—Error that remains after the transient has expired.

Summing Point—A descriptive symbol used in block diagrams to denote the algebraic summation of two or more signals; the direction of information flow is indicated by arrows, and the algebraic process of the summation by plus and minus signs.

Torque Constant—Constant of proportionality between motor stall torque and control voltage.

Transfer Function—A mathematical relationship between an input signal and a corresponding output signal; may be given in terms of LaPlace transforms and as the ratio of output to input.

Transient Response—Output versus time in response to a step input.

Undamped Natural Frequency (ω_D)—System oscillatory frequency when all damping is removed.

Velocity Lag Error—Lag between input and output that is proportional to the rate at which the input is varying.

Viscous Damping—Utilization of reactive torque, or force, proportional to speed for braking action.

Viscous Friction—Friction proportional to angular or linear speed.

Transfer functions

Device	Transfer Function	Dimensions
Potentiometer	$K_P = \dfrac{E_0}{\theta_{IN}}$	V/deg or V/rad
Synchro Pair CX-CT	$K_s = \dfrac{E_0}{\theta_{IN}}$	V/deg or V/rad
Linear Variable Differential Transformer	$K_{LVDT} = \dfrac{E_0}{DISPLACE}$	V/increment
Amplifier	$K_A = \dfrac{E_0}{E_{IN}}$	
Modulator	$K_M = \dfrac{E_0}{E_{IN}}$	AC volts/DC volts
Demodulator	$K_D = \dfrac{E_0}{E_{IN}}$	DC volts/AC volts
Gear Train	$\dfrac{I}{N} = \dfrac{\theta_0}{\theta_{IN}}$	
Rate Generator	$K_G s = \dfrac{E_0}{\theta_{IN}}$	V/1000 rpm or V/rad/s

Device	Transfer Function	Dimensions
AC Servomotor	$\dfrac{\theta_0}{E_{IN}} = \dfrac{K_T}{s(1 + s\tau_M)}$	deg/V or rad/V
DC Servomotor Armature Control	$\dfrac{\theta_0}{V_F} = \dfrac{K_{T/F}}{s[1 + (J/F)s](1 + s\tau_A)}$	deg/V or rad/V
DC Servomotor Field Control	$\dfrac{\theta_0}{V_F} = \dfrac{K_T}{R_F J s^2(1 + s\tau_F)(1 + s\tau_M)}$	deg/V or rad/V
Lag Network	$\dfrac{E_0}{E_{IN}} = \dfrac{1 + \tau_1 s}{1 + \tau_2 s}$	
Lead Network	$\dfrac{E_0}{E_{IN}} = \dfrac{1 + \tau_1 s}{1 + \tau_2 s}$	
AC Servomotor Inertial Damped	$\dfrac{\theta_0}{E_{IN}} = \dfrac{K_V(1 + \tau_2 s)}{(1 + \tau_1 s)(1 + \tau_3 s)}$	deg/V or rad/V
AC Servomotor Viscous Damped	$\dfrac{\theta_0}{E_{IN}} = \dfrac{K_V}{s(1 + \tau_M s)}$	deg/V or rad/V
Magnetic Amplifier	$\dfrac{E_0}{E_{IN}} = \dfrac{K}{(1 + \tau s)}$	Volts/Volt

Universal transient response curves

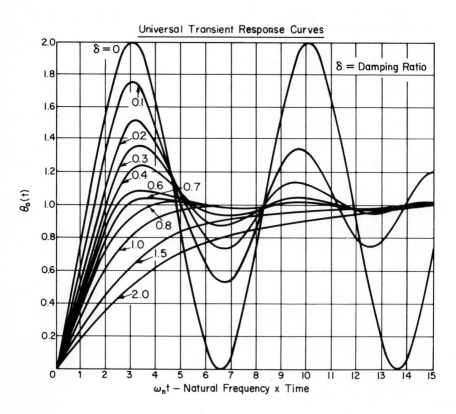

References

Ahrendt, W. R., *Servomechanism Practice*. New York: McGraw-Hill Book Company, 1954.

Baeck, Henry, *Practical Servomechanisms Design*. New York: McGraw-Hill Book Company, 1968.

Bateson, Robert, *Introduction to Control System Technology*. Columbus, Ohio: Charles E. Merrill Publishing Company, 1973.

Brite, Robert, and Carlo Fioranelli, *Synchros and Servos*. Indianapolis, Ind.: Howard Sams, 1967.

Bukstein, E., *Basic Servomechanisms*. New York: Holt, Rinehart & Winston, 1963.

Bulliet, L. J., *Servomechanisms*. Reading, Mass.: Addison Wesley Publishing Company, 1967.

Chestnut, Harold, and Robert Mayer, *Servomechanisms and Regulating System Design*. New York: John Wiley & Sons, 1951.

DC Motors, Speed Controls, Servo Systems. Hopkins, Minn.: Electrocraft Corporation, 1973.

DeRoy, Benjamin E., *Automatic Control Theory*. New York: John Wiley & Sons, 1966.

Hagen, Frank, *Servo Engineers Handbook*. Worcester, Pa.: Transicoil Inc., 1968.

Herceg, E., *Handbook of Measurement and Control*. Pennsauken, N.J.: Schaevitz Engineering, 1972.

Humphrey, William, *Introduction to Servo System Design*. Englewood Cliffs, N.J.: Prentice-Hall, Inc., 1973.

Johnson, Eric R., *Servomechanisms.* Englewood Cliffs, N.J.: Prentice-Hall, Inc., 1963.

Kearfott, *Technical Information for the Engineer—Number 1.* Little Falls, N.J.: Singer-General Precision, Inc., 1969.

Philco Technological Center, *Servomechanisms, Fundamentals and Experiments.* Englewood Cliffs, N.J.: Prentice-Hall, Inc., 1964.

The Singer Company, *AC Instrumentation Application Notes.* Los Angeles, Calif.: Singer Instrumentation, 1973.

Weyrick, Robert, *Fundamentals of Automatic Control.* New York: McGraw-Hill Book Company, 1975.

Zeines, B., *Automatic Control Systems.* Englewood Cliffs, N.J.: Prentice-Hall, Inc., 1972.

———, *Servomechanism Fundamentals.* New York, McGraw-Hill Book Company, 1959.

Answers to selected problems

CHAPTER 2

1. (b) 130.9°   (d) 1309°
3. 0°   360°
6. 0.0208%
7. 0.0476%
10. 5.357V
11. (b) 4.5V
20. 278°
22. Plastic—1.54W

CHAPTER 3

(see Chapter 4 problem 1)

CHAPTER 4

1. (c) −2.6V   (d) out-of-phase
2. (b) Altitude—4500 ft. Range—7790 ft.
3. (c) Slant range—12,650 ft. Elevation angle—71.6°
4. 6.2V 45°

5. (b) n − 36.4 mi.   w − 20.96 mi.

7. (b) E_{R2}—3.41V $E_{R1} = 9.4V$

8. (a) E_{S1}—5.0V $E_{S2} = -8.66V$ (c) Vector subtraction

CHAPTER 5

1. d

3. a

4. b

6. (c) $S_1 − S_2 = 78V, S_2 − S = 0, S_3 − S_1 = 78V$

9. a

10. (a) 120°

11. −120° (240°)

13. 300°

15. 100°

17. a

CHAPTER 6

1. (a) $E_0 = \dfrac{R2}{R_1 + R_2} E_1$

2. (a) $E_0 = E_1 \dfrac{R_2}{R_1} - E_0 \dfrac{R_2}{R_1}$

3. $\dfrac{C}{R} = \dfrac{A + B}{1 + HA}$

4. $R = 6$ $C = 450$

7. $\dfrac{C}{R} = \dfrac{G_1 G_2 (G_3 + G_4)}{G_1 G_2 (G_3 + G_4) + H(G_3 + G_4) + 1}$

9. $\dfrac{C}{R} = 56.3$

11. $\dfrac{C}{R} = \dfrac{G_1 G_2}{1 + H_1 G_1 + H_2 G_1 G_2}$

CHAPTER 7

1. 377 rad/s
2. 2800 rpm
4. 2 rpm
6. 0.833 sec.
9. 24,000 rad/s^2
10. 1500 rpm
14. 52.4%

CHAPTER 8

1. V = 70V   S = 875 rpm   T = 1225 oz-in
   V = 30V   S = 375 rpm   T = 525 oz-in
2. 89
4. (a) 0.01 oz.in/rad/s   (b) 200 sec

6. $\dfrac{\theta_0}{E} = \dfrac{4.06}{s(1 + 18.8s)}$

7. (a) 10V
8. 1250 rpm

10. $\dfrac{\theta_0}{E} = \dfrac{1020}{s(38 + s)}$

CHAPTER 9

3. (a) 11.92 oz.in/°   (b) 18.92 oz.in-sec/rad.
4. 4.86 Hz
6. (a) 6.66°   (b) 5.3°   (c) 0.0833 sec   (d) 0.108 sec
8. (a) 14.2°

CHAPTER 10

7. (a) -34.5dB, $-175°$
9. (a) 11.5dB and $-194°$, -29dB and $-242°$, -37dB and $-249°$
   (b) $\omega_{GC} = 3.87$ $\omega_{PC} = 0$
   (c) $\theta_{PM} = -25.5°$ $\theta_{GM} = 50$dB$^+$

11. (a) $\dfrac{C}{R} = \dfrac{45}{J\omega[1 + J(\omega/8)]}$

(d) $\omega_{BP} = 8$

(e) $\omega_{GC} = 19 \qquad \omega_{PC} = \infty$

(f) $\theta_{PM} = 22°$

(g) $-1dB$

(h) $21dB$ or $K = 11.22$

Index

INVENTORY 1C

INVENTORY 1983